PENGUI
EMPOWER

Ajay Poddar is an entrepreneur who graduated in civil engineering from the Indian Institute of Technology, Delhi in 1976. His current business interests are consulting, supply and installation of automatic mechanical multilevel parking systems, bottling of liquefied petroleum gas and space energizing of built spaces—homes, offices and plants using a new practice called environics. This science has been developed by him and his colleagues after fifteen years of research and learning from ancient and modern sciences, and energizing of more than 500 establishments, big and small.

He has been associated with children's welfare and is currently the chairman of SIDH, an NGO doing pioneering work in the Garhwal region on primary education and curriculum and skills development. He is a member of the managing committee and the chairman, energy committee, of the PHDCCI, an apex body of trade and business in northern and central India.

Ajay is also a reiki master and a pranic healer and is interested in music and poetry. He has travelled extensively in Europe, Africa and Asia on work, to give talks and promote environics.

Empower Yourself

New Life Solutions for Health and Well-being

AJAY PODDAR

With best wishes
to Lata and her
family

A big hurrah to
your creativity and
talent.
Mesmerized by
your persona

Ajay
15/6/09

PENGUIN BOOKS

PENGUIN BOOKS
Published by the Penguin Group
Penguin Books India Pvt. Ltd, 11 Community Centre, Panchsheel Park, New Delhi 110 017, India
Penguin Group (USA) Inc., 375 Hudson Street, New York, New York 10014, USA
Penguin Group (Canada), 90 Eglinton Avenue East, Suite 700, Toronto, Ontario, M4P 2Y3, Canada (a division of Pearson Penguin Canada Inc.)
Penguin Books Ltd, 80 Strand, London WC2R 0RL, England
Penguin Ireland, 25 St Stephen's Green, Dublin 2, Ireland (a division of Penguin Books Ltd)
Penguin Group (Australia), 250 Camberwell Road, Camberwell, Victoria 3124, Australia (a division of Pearson Australia Group Pty Ltd)
Penguin Group (NZ), 67 Apollo Drive, Rosedale, North Shore 0632, New Zealand (a division of Pearson New Zealand Ltd)
Penguin Group (South Africa) (Pty) Ltd, 24 Sturdee Avenue, Rosebank, Johannesburg 2196, South Africa

Penguin Books Ltd, Registered Offices: 80 Strand, London WC2R 0RL, England

First published by Penguin Books India 2007

Copyright © Ajay Poddar 2007

10 9 8 7 6 5 4 3 2

ISBN-13: 978-0-14310-384-4   ISBN-10: 0-14310-384-9

Typeset in Sabon by Mantra Virtual Services, New Delhi
Printed at Chaman Offset Printers, New Delhi

This book is my offering to my father, Vijay Poddar, on his seventy-fifth birthday. He made me experience the pleasures of goodness and spread a bouquet of values, some of which I may have imbibed.

I also dedicate it to the late Navajata, chairman of the Sri Aurobindo Society at Pondicherry, who told me to do things my way and to be myself, and not what others hoped or expected me to be.

Contents

Acknowledgements

At the outset I must acknowledge that this book would not have been written and published if I did not know Royina Grewal. She not only introduced me to Penguin, her publishers, but edited and re-edited chapters and made me realize that my convent school English was in tatters.

I acknowledge the great contribution of Prabhat Poddar, who taught me the use of the Lecher Antenna and led me to explore and develop an interest in much that I have written about. Some of his pioneering research has been included in the book.

I am grateful to my friend, Geetika Deepen, who helped me immensely with the synopsis and in structuring and writing the initial chapters. My sincere and grateful thanks to my colleague Manisha Matanhelia, who helped me write the text, put the graphics and visuals together and discover a lot of the knowledge which forms the core of the book.

I must express my gratitude to Pavan Varma (director general, Indian Council for Cultural Relations), who motivated me to write and invited me for talks at Cyprus, while he was the Indian ambassador there, and at the Nehru Centre in London.

I am thankful to Penguin, my publishers, and more particularly, Ravi Singh and V.K. Karthika, who encouraged and guided me. I am grateful to Veena Baswani for the insights and inputs given while editing the book.

In the end, I thank my wife, Nalini, my son, Pranav, my daughter, Shweta, and my parents for their understanding and support.

Introduction

Why should you read this book? What difference will it make to your life?

This book will give you a new perspective about yourself, about others and about your environment.

It will open a few doors, let fresh air into your life and enable you to see a perspective that you did not know existed. This will hopefully arouse your curiosity leading you to ask more questions, to seek more answers both from within and without, to create new vistas for yourself.

It will share traditional knowledge, belief systems and practices, and provide insights on what led to these practices—their bases and the scientific reasons behind them. It will explore how they need to be adapted to modern living with the help of new technology and research, and how they can be effectively used today.

This book will also empower you with simple Do It Yourselves, which can improve your health, your relationships and effectiveness in whatever you do.

The 11 chapters of the book will traverse a gamut of colours; symbols; healing systems; the energies emanating from the earth, other planets, built spaces and objects, and the subtle energies of the body, selecting the essentials that can be easily understood and validated to provide a new meaning to our existence and enhance the quality of our lives.

Do you know that . . .?

- We are deficient in the colours that we really like excessively and crave for.
- Our earth has a magnetic core which emanates grid lines or grid walls in north to south and east to west directions at regular intervals along the earth's surface, and animals can locate these lines.
- There is magic and, therefore, sanctity in the number 108.
- Music and sounds can convert into light and images.
- A man's height is nine times the length of his palm and a woman's height is eight times the length of her palm.
- Microwave cooking destroys the nutrition value of all foods except fish.

Find out about this and unravel much, much more by reading on . . .

> *'Analyzing the mind is a little like pulling apart a radio in search of the music.'*
>
> —Robert Tomney

We go through life working, eating, sleeping, entertaining, rationalizing, copulating and complaining. We experience big highs and debilitating lows. Often life is a roller-coaster ride. If things are even and smooth, life seems to be uneventful and boring. We look for ways to generate excitement, by creating new situations or friendships, changing our environment and in a myriad other ways.

In spite of receiving the best education, easy access to latest information and the best comforts and conveniences, the problems of stress, soured relationships, lack of satisfaction with our work and our achievements seem to persist. We tend to run after things and set goals which appear meaningless before we are halfway through.

Perhaps this happens because we set goals and pursue activities due to peer pressure or because they are considered to be the 'in' things. Very often, what we do for leisure and entertainment ends up causing stress rather than giving us satisfaction and comfort.

Whether it is a choice of career options, of what to buy, how to live or how to decorate our house, we seem to do things which other people approve of and not because we really want or need them.

Clearly we need to approach life with a different perspective, greater understanding of our environment, the people around us and ourselves.

We Need New Life Solutions!

It often escapes our mind that ancient civilizations were prosperous and highly advanced. They created amazing monuments, concepts and thoughts—all this without the kind of access to knowledge and technology that we have. Today we are able to do more in less time: we can access information and entertainment online with a click of a mouse within seconds. We have more amenities and can travel faster. The obvious question then is: Why are we so prone to illness, stress and discord? Were the ancients more knowledgeable than we think they were? Did they use techniques and practices that we have lost or discarded? Did they lead a lifestyle more conducive to good health and harmony? Did they possess a greater intrinsic understanding and acceptance of their own selves and surroundings than we do?

Ever since the Industrial Revolution, it is the thoughts and actions of the Western world that have almost completely guided and dictated norms of living to the rest of the world. Till recently, modern thought only recognized the physical dimensions of energy and differentiated between mind and matter. Logic was regarded as reality, and intuition as imagination.

Intuition

The Eastern mind recognizes the validity of intuition as a fundamental tool for decision making, because it recognizes that consciousness is supreme, and thought, emotional response and physical activity are all projections of this consciousness. What the Western mind forgets is that all scientific discoveries were made when people ventured into the realm of the unknown and the unproven. After they experienced the same phenomenon again and again, they established its validity through experiments. Only after this had been done, the phenomenon or the discovery was structured into a matrix of logic!

Modern scientific research has proved that during our lifetime we only use 5-10 per cent of our brain or mental faculties. This means that there is a large amount of knowledge, information, experience and insight within us, which we are not aware of. We do not know how to access this storehouse and take out what we need to improve our quality of life.

Eastern philosophers and the ancients recognized that the best way to tap large parts of the brain was to connect with 'intuition'. We all use intuition or our sixth sense on innumerable occasions. When we instantly dislike a person, even though he may come across as being well mannered and well dressed, it is our intuition at work. Many a time we avoid situations or encounters because we have a premonition that the meeting in question will not bode well.

There are things that we just 'seem to know', or which come to us as a 'déjà vu' or a flash. Sometimes we disregard these flashes since there does not seem to be any logic to them. However, very often we realize that had we followed the directives of our inner mind, that is, our intuition, we would have been better off.

To connect with intuition, try this exercise:

Visualize your whole house, inside and outside. What do you see? Only one view—the front, or the back or the side. To see the entire house you would try to put these images together. Obviously there would be unmatched, jagged edges and the picture would not be something which you would enjoy or hold in your consciousness. This is what logic does for us. It breaks up and digitizes reality. When we connect with our intuition we can see the whole house together, inside and outside, at the same time—as a complete harmonious whole.

The Eastern mind recognizes that energy has mental, emotional, physical and psychic dimensions that are inseparable.

Practices like meditation and yoga have now become very popular in the west as people have found that, through them, they are able to reduce their anxiety levels and create a state of equanimity. The direct physical manifestation is a reduction in the pulse rate. It is commonly accepted that a lower pulse rate indicates a better state of health and increases longevity.

We know that when we are calm we are able to listen better to our mind and body. This means that we are hearing or accessing a part of the brain we could not earlier because of the tumult within. The more we listen to this inner voice, the calmer we become, and are able to conquer more milestones and reach higher summits of achievement.

Animals and birds thrive on intuition. Given a choice, they avoid spaces with negative energy, unless certain types of negative energies are beneficial to them. For example, dogs, sheep, cows, horses and most other animals tend to sit or sleep on zones of high positive energy. Cats, bees and ants seek zones and nodes of negative energy since their bodies need negative electrostatic charge to be energized.

Thousands of birds fly hundreds of miles in structured formations after each season to another location. The magnetite cells in their bodies enable them to know their position with respect to the latitudinal and longitudinal forces of the earth on account of which they can reach exactly where they have to. They possess the sensitivity to listen to these cells of their body.

Animals, birds and children seem to have boundless energy. Even when they fall they do not seem to get injured as adults do since their bodies intuitively position themselves correctly to minimize injury.

We have often heard people say that they do not have enough time to do things that they wish to. The intuitive mind is capable of creating a lot of free time for us. It enables us to take decisions faster without procrastination and fear, and lo and behold! We have the luxury of more free time for other things!

Value Systems

Apart from intuition, what perhaps helped people in ancient civilizations were their value systems. Unlike modern man, they did not perceive themselves as individual entities. They intrinsically understood and accepted the deep connection with other fellow beings, nature, the earth's energies and cosmic forces. People were encouraged to consider themselves as trustees and not owners of wealth or knowledge.

Within families, people performed different functions. One person pursued religion, another fought for the country, the third did social work, the fourth earned money, while another looked after the children, the animals and the agriculture. The breadwinner did not grudge his income being shared by others. All pursuits were considered to be equally important and contributory to the well-being of the family and the community.

Within the social hierarchy, a shoemaker was given his due recognition, and his utility and value to the community was accorded almost the same amount of respect as that given to a goldsmith or a mathematician. No profession was looked down upon or considered less relevant.

The same unity of thought and purpose was relevant for the country and the world at large.

History is replete with accounts of scholars from China and South America who travelled to India, and vice versa. They travelled for years in quest of knowledge and understanding. Language did not pose any barrier and there are no reports about their being unwelcome. *'Bahujan hitaye bahujan sukhaye'*—An act is good if it is for the welfare and happiness of most people. *'Atithee devah bhava'*—A guest is God. *'Vasudaiva kutumbakam'*—The world is one family. The ancients followed these thoughts in letter and spirit!

Leading a Holistic Life

In addition to their life's work, our ancestors' daily routine consisted of exercise, prayer, rituals, listening to and imbibing from elders, learning traditional crafts, and understanding the effects of the sun, moon and planets. They performed various functions at specified times of the day and night. Individual spaces were associated with different elements: they were sanctified for specific activities relating to each element. For example, the sun, which signifies heat and fire, moves from the south-east to the north-west. It therefore made sense that the kitchen should be located in either of these areas. Various colours and symbols, both religious and artistic, like the *navgraha* and *rangoli* were used to create energy fields and bestow beneficial effects. Our ancestors had access to medical practitioners of high learning and accomplishment, who could prescribe and prepare medicines from herbs and plants, and diagnose diseases by reading the pulse. They also knew how to orient themselves in space and wore rings, gems, stones or other trinkets for self-protection.

An architect or Vaastu *shastri* had to know all 64 arts and sciences known as *chaunsath kala*, before he was allowed to practice. He would stay at a site for about six months to sense the energies of the earth, observe changes of light, shadow and wind during various seasons and observe the movement of the sun, moon and other planets. He would also make intricate calculations based on the hand measurements of the owner of the property and his date of birth, before recommending what he perceived the dimensions of the length, width and height of the structure should be. It was only then that he began designing.

Ancient structures like the pyramids of Egypt and the Acropolis temple in Greece were designed on the basis of relationships between length, breadth and height, which were so precise that modern scientists are left wondering how they did so without the help of modern and advanced instruments. The accuracy of these proportions was surely a divine gift. Similarly, the Ashoka Pillar, in Delhi, is a metallurgical wonder. It is made of iron of a hundred per cent purity, which no one has been able to replicate even in the most advanced laboratory conditions.

New Thoughts and Research

Albert Einstein was the first to suggest that matter was nothing but vibration and it was possible to attain higher levels of energy with smaller forms by achieving greater amplitude and resonance. He pointed the way to quantum physics, nuclear energy and the microchip.

Ernst Lecher, a German physician, who practised medicine in the mid-1900s, found that different people staying in the same house contracted the same diseases. His experiments led him to develop a divining instrument called the Lecher Antenna, which could measure all the bio-electro-magnetic radiations which affect the cells of the human body. Similarly, around the same time, Seymour Kirlian, a Russian scientist, developed an instrument for electro-photography, to photograph the auras around a person and diagnose the state of his health. Since then many more accurate instruments for measuring and photographing subtle energies and radiations have been developed.

It is now possible to check the applicability, relevance and efficacy of certain interventions and practices, whether ancient or modern, medical or architectural, and modify and adapt them for the best results.

Modern medical practitioners readily admit that out of

say 1000 known diseases, they have cures only for thirty, while for the rest, they merely prescribe medication that retards or enhances the various chemical reactions in the body, thus facilitating the body's own ability to cure diseases. This is so because they try only to deal with the physical causes or symptoms of the disease.

On the other hand, the ancient sciences of medicine like homeopathy, ayurveda and unani developed their diagnostic and healing system1s by treating all the energies of the body— mental, physical, emotional and psychic, as an indivisible whole.

How and Why I Began This Journey?

Concerned about my manufacturing plant, which was closed, I was talking to an uncle of mine who lives in Hyderabad, a city considered to have the best practitioners of Vaastu Shastra. He looked at the site plan and asked me details about the slope of the land. After listening to what I said, he suggested that I dig a pit in the north-east corner and raise the south-west portion. I implemented his simple and inexpensive advice, without asking him why I should do so or how these measures would help.

The day the work was completed, a buyer walked into our office. I adopted a different approach and the whole transaction went through within six months. I was perplexed and grateful and thanked my benefactor.

Soon afterwards, my father brought home Prabhat, an architect living in Pondicherry. He explained some of the rationale behind ancient sciences like Astrology and Vaastu Shastra, elaborating on the original thoughts behind some of the rituals. I was hooked. He used a gizmo called the Lecher Antenna to measure the bio-electro-magnetic (BEM) radiations of people and spaces.

Around the same time, I contracted tuberculosis and another coincidence occurred. I got a note from a friend of mine who had studied with me at the Indian Institute of Technology, Delhi. She informed me that she was a reiki channel, and suggested that I too get learn to be a reiki channel from her reiki master, the following week.

Intrigued, I attended the First Level reiki session. The master told us that we would need to spend one and a half hours of practice on ourselves, for at least twenty-one days, to go on to the next level. Horrified, I exclaimed that I did not have that kind of time since I was busy from morning to night—working, socializing, playing—and did not, in fact, seem to have enough time to do any of these things satisfactorily. The master gently suggested that if that were the case, I should enjoy my cup of coffee and go away.

After allowing me to have a few sips and swallow my embarrassment, he ventured that if I made a commitment, time would make itself available to me. Something told me to agree: I followed the master, got attuned and became a reiki channel. This was to change my life.

After one day's practice, I found to my utter surprise and wonder that the next morning, I woke up one and a half hours earlier than usual. The same happened the next day and thereafter, without my feeling any extra fatigue. Reiki cured my tuberculosis in one month instead of the six months that it normally takes with medication.

Reiki helped create time and abundance for me. I was more often in a state of gratitude for what I had instead of agonizing over what I should have had by now and what others had and I did not. I was able to finish my work and other commitments well in time. I could take decisions without prevaricating for hours. Reiki made me more intuitive and gave me the courage to trust my instincts and the ability to hear the voice within. It made the purpose of my life clear— to fulfil myself and to help and learn from others by understanding them.

After reiki, I went on a learning spree. I did other levels of reiki, pranic healing, Arhatic yoga and Lecher Antenna training within six months. My business also improved.

I spent hours, days and months over a period of ten years, discussing, researching, consulting and giving talks on topics such as space energizing, subtle energies and colours. I continue to do so when I can. I am pleased that the business and scientific community, as well as the media, is beginning to realize the immense benefits that this and other unexplored knowledge systems promise to deliver.

Sharing Life's Solutions

Our organization, Syenergy Environics Ltd, conducts path-breaking consultancy which entails energy correction and enhancement for clients—both corporate and individuals, for homes, factories and offices. This is done after acquainting ourselves about the past history of the organization, its issues and concerns, the state of health of the people using the space and their future aspirations.

Most of the knowledge systems discussed in this book and some others, which concern energizing and correcting health and space, that are practised by us, have been nomenclated 'Environics'. Our organization comprises a young team of professionals, which I hope will grow in numbers. We are fortunate to have people on our Board of Directors and Advisory Council who are not only highly accomplished in their own vocations, but caring human beings. Without their commitment and support, much of the little that has been achieved may not have been possible.

This book will have achieved its purpose if it encourages you, dear reader and fellow traveller, to journey into your own undiscovered and abundant spaces bravely and with an open mind, and share your insights with others towards enriching them as you will have been enriched yourselves.

Happy journey!

2

Subtle Energies of the Human Body

There is nothing that is unknown or impossible,
Only large gaps in our knowledge and endeavour.

The two words 'subtle' and 'energy' used together do not mean anything to most people. Let us try to explain why we use them together.

We all know that what is achieved by subtle nuances is not possible with obvious gestures. A look can often 'speak' volumes and communicate a message more eloquently than speech or gestures.

'Subtle' means something which requires sensitivity to comprehend and appreciate. It is not necessarily something full of mystery, otherworldly or esoteric.

'Energy' is normally associated with a force, unseen but real, which drives men and machines. It lights up homes, makes us fly, processes billions of megabytes of information and enables us to conquer unknown frontiers of knowledge.

What most of us do not perceive are the other energies emanating from the earth, the planets, other living beings, gemstones and other objects considered to be inanimate. Little is known about how they affect our being every nanosecond and how they interact with our body.

It is now an accepted scientific fact that matter does not create energy but energy creates matter. Energy can be emitted by symbols, cosmic and earth radiations and vibrations of cells in the atmosphere, or in the human body; it can create light, sound, electricity, movement and matter.

Earlier, conventional science believed that to use large amounts of energy we had to generate and store similar or larger amounts. We had mountains and rooms full of gigantic computers, large turbines and mammoth machines. With the discovery of Quantum Physics and its application to generate new thought and technology, the smallest, unmeasured atom can now store more energy and release it with greater force than thousands of turbines and rockets. The smallest microchip can store and process more information than armies of gigantic computers.

We all know that the mind thinks. Thoughts create vibration, vibration energy and energy matter. We all make affirmations and resolutions which often manifest into reality or materalize.

Do you accept that the heart and all the other organs and cells of the body can 'think', process information and perform various functions, sometimes in co-ordination with one another and when required, even on their own?

This is best illustrated by the **coma** story. We know that when a person goes into coma and remains in that state for years sometimes, his body keeps functioning normally. This proves that each cell of the body can exist on its own and function efficiently without being directed by the brain.

Another amazing example in medical science is when somebody's writing thumb is amputated and doctors replace it with a toe from the person's foot. After about six months, the toe takes the shape of the thumb.

The cells of our body have the ability to rebuild themselves and vibrate and resonate with one another in perfect harmony. They strive to regain that balance when disturbed and therefore heal the body.

The Physical Body

The physical human body is a phenomenon that has been studied minutely over the years. It can be photographed and x-rayed. The location of the body's organs, their size and shape, how they connect with nerves and arteries, and how they process air, food and water to give us sustenance, nourishment and the energy to walk, talk and accomplish many other things—these physiological details have been mastered by medical science. But, in spite of the most advanced medical research, there are so many reactions within the physical body, which defy comprehension. **Where can we look for the answers? Is there more?**

The Subtle Body

Surrounding the physical body is the subtle body—more powerful and versatile. The image of the subtle body interacting with, enveloping and protecting the physical body has been projected from time immemorial by men of all cultures, as a glow emanating from the bodies of saints or a halo around the head of deities. Descriptions of a swirling field of energy surrounding the human body can be found in our ancient texts. The Hindus call this body of energy 'Prana' —life-giving force, the Australians—'Kuranita', the Polynesians—'Manas', the Chinese—'Chi', and the Greeks referred to it as 'Microcosmic Egg—the brilliant clouds in which men live and move'. This energy field of the human body or our subtle body is commonly known as **AURA,** a Latin word, meaning 'gently moving air' and 'a glow of light'.

The aura of a person is a force field described in Hindu Vedic literature as the 'Pranamaya Kosha'—The storehouse of life-giving energy, and in modern science as the ionic-charged layer surrounding living substances.

What are ions? They are particles of energy that charge the atmosphere and energize people. Gadgets called ionizers, are now being increasingly used in offices to improve the quality of air. The abundance of ions near the sea and in the hills makes us feel good.

When we are in the company of spiritual or learned people, we feel energized and happy. Their presence itself has a calming effect that stays with us. We often say that we have been *touched* by them. Indeed we are touched by their aura, which can sometimes extend over large physical distances. For example, the presence of the Dalai Lama in many large gatherings profoundly benefits people. Not many remember what he actually said but, nevertheless, feel good for many days thereafter.

Basically what happens is that the aura of such people envelops us, enhancing the vibration of the cells of our own aura, which, in turn, becomes larger in size. A larger aura indicates better health, just like a well-exercised and muscular physical body.

The acceptance of the phenomena of the subtle body or aura becomes easier when we realize that the body itself is not a mere solid, physical entity. Within the scientific realm it is now recognized that the physical body does not comprise solely a solid mass of bones, flesh and skin, but innumerable densely packed cells. When these cells are less densely structured, they cannot be touched and are termed as the aura.

Einstein, perhaps the greatest scientist of the last century, conducted experiments on the body and its cellular structure. He proved that the smallest cell of the human body is not an identifiable physical entity. When examined under the microscope the human cells looked like a number of streamers, which on further examination, seemed to almost dissolve into nothingness.

The physical body as we know it, is enveloped by and interacts with the inner and the outer auras, which are actually an integral part of our persona and being. Normally, the inner aura extends between 1 to 3 metres and the outer aura between 5 to 15 metres. Ever so often we sense the presence of someone in a large gathering and turn back to see whether he/she is there. What is really happening is that the aura of a familiar person is coming into contact with our aura and is emanating signals or vibrations which are recognized by us.

Auras that were once assumed to be mythical or imaginary can now be photographed by Kirlian photography, or more scientifically, electro-photography. This was popularized by Seymon Kirlian of Russia, who photographed the aura around the fingers by passing a low current through the body at a high voltage which caused a sudden discharge of ions from the fingers. A lot of fascinating research has been carried out in Russia and the US in what is popularly called 'capturing the human aura'. Under normal circumstances in a zone free of negative energies, the aura has an even distribution consisting of a cloud-like inert zone, called the Corona and a filamentous outer zone termed as Streamers.

Kirlian photography is used often in medical science and research to determine the state of health of a person. In an experiment conducted by us the Kirlian photographs of a patient in a hospital indicated that the person was probably in an advanced stage of cancer. The corona was distorted and the streamers had almost disappeared. However, when the radiations present in the room from the overhead water tanks, magnetic lines of the earth, the television set, electrical power source and other medical equipment were neutralized and the photographs taken again, we were astounded to see that the aura became almost normal and the patient showed no signs of cancer. All electromagnetic radiations from electrical gadgets and appliances are harmful for the body since the A/C currents, which drive them, subject the body to severe trauma because it switches from + to − fifty times per second (see Fig. 2.1). Simple and effective ways to counter their effects by using colours and symbols have been found and will be detailed later.

Presently, only the inner aura can be photographed. A part of it, approximately 2-6 inches wide, known as the etheric body, can be seen visually by clairvoyants as a profusion of swirling colours. (Clairvoyants are men and women who have a heightened visual and sensory ability.) More women than men have this ability, perhaps because of their higher sensitivity, which can be further developed with basic training and some

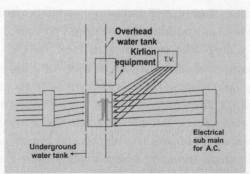

Fig. 2.1 Human Body Subjected to Various
EM Radiations

meditation. The outer aura can be sensed, felt and scanned by hand. (Try this: rub your palms against one another for about thirty seconds. Press the centre of the palms with the thumb. Move the palms away from one another and slowly bring them together. When they come closer, you may feel pressure or resistance which increases as the palms come closer. This can be felt when we place our palms on the sides of a person's head or any part of the body. For different parts, the same pressure or sensation will be felt at different distances. For strong and healthy auras, the pressure can be felt from farther away and for weak or depleted auras, much closer to the body.) People can be trained to do so.

Other than clairvoyants, all of us at some moment or other in our lives have seen the etheric aura and the particles of energy. When we sometimes get up from sleep, especially in the afternoon, or when we are just gazing at the sky looking at nothing in particular, we often see some silver streaks and globules swirling in front of our eyes. These are the vital energies—prana or ions, which are present in our surroundings and enter our physical body.

During our workshops, held during the day, we make people look at the open sky for a while. After a few minutes, they start seeing particles and globules. Then we make them look at the outline of trees and buildings and gradually people can see a layer surrounding the outermost portion of the leaves or the buildings that does not quite look like the rest of the sky. It looks thicker, has a certain width and shows moving particles and colours. These are the auras of the plants and the buildings. High-precision photography confirms that not only human beings, but plants, buildings, animals and all other animate and inanimate objects and beings have auras. However, there are many who insist that these particles are seen only due to retinal image retention. (When you have been looking at an object for a long time, the image of the object stays in our vision for a few seconds thereafter. This is known as retinal image retention.) The obvious question then is, why does the deficiency not occur again for months or years in some cases?

The physical body, inner and outer aura can be likened to ice, water and vapour, respectively, which are all various forms of the same entity and convert constantly into one another. We perceive them differently because the so-called vibratory matter is packed densely or tightly in one form, say ice, or the physical body; less densely in water or the inner aura which can both be seen and photographed, and in a finer form in vapour or the outer aura, which can neither be seen nor photographed.

A healthy person's aura is large and full of bright colours, whereas an unhealthy person has an aura, which is smaller and full of dull colours, such as greys and browns, especially around the part of the body, which is diseased. When a person is near death the aura almost completely disappears. This happens because the 'chakras', which are the organs of the subtle body, and are explained in subsequent paragraphs, dissolve and stop functioning and sustaining the aura.

How Does the AURA Help?

Auras act as buffers between the outer environment and the physical body and filter sensations, radiations and disease. A person starts feeling unwell before actually falling sick or has a sense of foreboding before a major calamity. The radiations enter the subtle body before reaching the physical body, giving us timely indication to rest, or take medication and prevent the disease, or to move away from a place or a particular situation to avert the impending calamity.

An experiment was conducted in a hospital at Pondicherry on fifty people suspected to have cancer. In the biopsy tests, twenty-five of them tested positive. The Lecher Antenna was used to detect the disease on the same fifty people. The Antenna is a versatile and precise dousing instrument which can detect and scan the whole spectrum of electromagnetic radiations that have any effect on the body, including cancer radiations. In the test forty-five persons tested positive. The twenty (the forty-five who tested positive with the Antenna minus the twenty-five who tested positive in the biopsy) whose biopsy tests were clear, were called one month later for another biopsy. All of them tested positive. This established that the disease had entered the aura more than a month ago. If treated then, the physical body could have been saved from the manifestation of the disease. Moreover, if they had not been asked to return, these twenty people would have gone back reassured that they did not suffer from cancer and would not therefore have received treatment. In most cases, persons with a clear biopsy test only go back for the next test after severe discomfort; by then, the disease is in an advanced stage and cannot be treated.

Chakras and Naadis

Similar to the system of organs and arteries in the physical body, the subtle body consists of a complex system of chakras, or energy vortexes, which absorb energies from the environment and expel energies processed by the body system. They are cones of energy spinning in rhythmic rotation. They transmute energy through a network of energy circuits called naadis or meridians. These cannot be seen, as they are part of the subtle body or aura.

However, they are connected to the organs and the nerves

of the physical body and empower and direct them to perform various functions (see colour insert 'The Chakras').

There are hundreds of chakras in the subtle body, but the seven major chakras are located along the spine from the base of the spine to the top of the head. Several minor chakras are located all over the body, at all the joints, in the palms of the hands and the soles of the feet. Each chakra corresponds to a particular set of body organs; systems; glands and hormones; emotional, mental and psychic functions. They are also identified with a particular colour, sound and element. (Refer to Table 2.1, p. 25).

Chakras and naadis have been an integral part of ancient knowledge in India and a basis of healing. It has been recorded that the chakras rotate clockwise and anticlockwise, fifty times per second (an A/C current also completes fifty cycles per second). When they rotate clockwise they draw in energy, and expel processed or used energy into the environment while moving anticlockwise. When a chakra dysfunctions or becomes clogged, its speed and frequency of movement reduces. This means that it is absorbing less energy than required by the body and expelling only a part of the energy processed by the body, which needs to be thrown out. The retention of negative energy in the body and the inability of the body to draw in enough fresh energy results in aggravation of the disease.

A chakra can be over or under energized, balanced, open or blocked. Symptoms of a disease are mirrored by dysfunction within the related energy network and the chakra itself. The nature of dysfunction can be detected by scanners, dowsers, etc., and can be treated by various healing methods like reiki, t'ai chi, acupressure, acupuncture, deep breathing, meditation and medical intervention which can restore the chakras and the subtle body system to its original state of balance.

Colours, chanting of mantras or hymns, wearing gemstones and musical notes can also be used for energizing the chakras. Table 2.1 shows the corresponding colour, musical note, mantra, planet, *yantra* forms (shapes and symbols) and gems relating to each chakra. It has been found that each of these has the same wavelength and vibratory frequency. Thus they resonate like two tuning forks or two musical instruments correctly tuned. When one is played or vibrated, the other one picks up the vibration and plays automatically, the resonance creating an enhanced effect. Today music therapy is being increasingly used in a lot of hospitals along with colour projections.

Deep breathing, rubbing of palms, placing palms around a candle flame and chanting are effective methods of energizing the chakras and keeping the body healthy.

Positive and Negative Energy

Ancient medicinal systems recognized that the energy of bacteria or germs need not be destroyed, but the nature of their vibrations can be changed to convert them from negative to positive. This is best illustrated by homeopathy. A drop of the concentrate of the bacteria which needs to be treated is shaken vigorously with 1000 drops of water; one drop out of this is again mixed with 1000 drops of water, and the process is repeated again and again, anywhere between six to 200 times. The milder or weaker the mixture, the more potent it becomes. When administered to the patient, it changes the vibratory field of the same germ within the body.

Table 2.1: Chakras and Their Relationship with Elements, Planets, etc.

Chakras	Muladhara	Swadisthan	Manipura	Anahat	Vishudha	Ajna	Shasasradhara
Nerve Plexus	Sacral Plexus (Root)	Prosatic Plexus	Solar Plexus	Cardiac Plexus (Heart)	Laryngeal Plexus (Throat)	Cavernous Plexus (Eyebrow)	Crown
Element	Earth	Water	Fire	Air	Ether	Second Sight	Spirit
Colour	Red	Orange	Yellow	Green	Blue	Indigo	Violet
Lecher Wavelength	7.30	11.0	11.5	10.3	13.2	5.0	4.05
Music Note	C	D	E	F	G	A	B
Bij Mantra	'Lam'	'Vam'	'Ram'	'Yam'	'Ham'	'Om'	—
Planet	Saturn	Jupiter	Mars	Venus	Mercury	Sun	Moon
Yantra Form	Square	Circle	Triangle	Crescent	Bindu	Spiral	—
Gems	Sapphire	Topaz	Coral	Diamond	Emerald	Ruby	Pearl

Human Energy Axis

We know logically that anything that rotates must do so around an axis. However, neither the scriptures nor any other recorded material has described how these chakras rotate. During the last ten years, Dr Prabhat Poddar and others carried out experiments using the Lecher Antenna and discovered, validated, measured and documented various types of human energy axes. It was found that the human body has energy fields at the front and the back of the body. Each field consists of four axes: vertical, horizontal, diagonal and perpendicular (see Fig. 2.2).

Each type of axis represents a particular kind of energy. The vertical axis represents physical energies, the horizontal— mental, the diagonal—emotional, and the perpendicular— psychic. Often, more than one or even all axes are disturbed because physical, mental, emotional and psychic energies are interrelated and impact each other. For example, when a person has fever, in addition to being physically weak, he is also emotionally vulnerable and mentally irritable.

Eastern systems of medicine like Ayurveda recognize the deep connection between the mind and body. They understand, diagnose and treat the subtle body as an extension of the physical body. Alleviation of discomfort and disease depends on our ability to become mentally aware of the cause—be it emotional, psychic or physical, and then to balance the mind and extend that balance to the body.

Children and animals are particularly receptive and sensitive to the signals of their aura/subtle bodies. We often see them restlessly moving around in sleep till their body locates the least disturbing zone and orients itself accordingly. They also generally avoid harmful food and overeating and the company of certain beings unless forced by adults and masters.

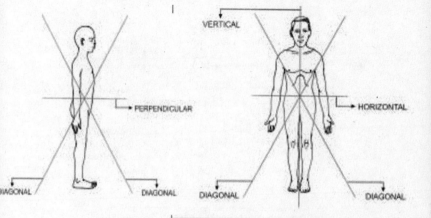

Fig. 2.2 Four Orientations of Human Energy Axes

Work with the Lecher Antenna has also helped us discover that besides having four axes, the body can be further divided into four parts, relating to different segments of the body. These are the mental—head zone, vital/emotional—trunk zone, physical—leg zone, and psychic—entire body. If the energy axes intersect in the centre of the body, the person is in a state of good health. A displaced axis indicates various degrees of ill health and mental and emotional disturbance, depending on the extent of displacement.

An axis can be easily displaced in the body when it is subjected to direct radiation from a television set, music system, cell phone, microwave, air conditioner and other electrical appliances that work on alternating current. In addition, radiation from underground water streams, incorrect orientation while sitting or sleeping, and other phenomena can cause displacement of an axis. An alternate current, as stated earlier, fluctuates between positive and negative and flows fifty times a second, which causes severe trauma to the cells of the body. D/C or direct current, is not harmful.

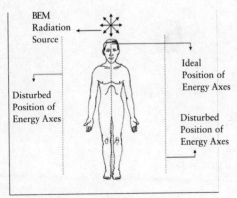

Fig. 2.3 Effect of EM Radiation on Axis

The most common reason for displacement of an axis and ill health is incorrect orientation of the body with respect to the magnetic forces of the earth that are much stronger than the energy intensity of the human body. The energy axis of the body is centred and aligned when the person is facing north or east during daytime and south or east at night. While asleep, an individual's head should be towards the south or east, so that when he gets up, he should be facing the north or the west. This is applicable to the northern hemisphere. The directions for the southern hemisphere are different, with the south being substituted by the north and vice versa.

Warning: The next time you go for an MRI scan, check that the machine is placed so that your body is not oriented incorrectly when lying down. Otherwise the results may not be accurate. You may end up having surgery when it is not required. Let me explain how. MRI stands for Magnetic Resonance Imaging, which is a photographing technique. It records the position of the magnetite cells in the human body or around the affected region to diagnose the extent of damage. If the body is not oriented correctly the cells will be more displaced than usual and can lead the medical practitioner to decide on treatment which he would not prescribe if he saw an MRI of the person whose body was correctly oriented.

It has also been found that the energy axis measured during the day, completely disappears at sunset and is soon substituted by another set of axes which may or may not show the same level of disturbance or alignment. Experiments showed that the body exhibits different energy axes during the sun period (sunrise to sunset), moon period (moonrise to moonset), and earth period (when there is no son or moon). The longest earth period in a day is on Amavasya, the day when there is no moon, and the shortest period in a day is on a full moon day.

Hand Mudras

To use these axes for our benefit we use mudras or hand postures. These include various combinations of touching the thumb with each finger to attain concentration and isolation of energies in different parts of the body.

These mudras are commonly used in yoga and meditation for improving health and attaining higher states of concentration and consciousness. If the thumb is positioned at the tip of the index finger, it activates the mental energy axis. Similarly, the thumb on middle finger activates the vital/emotional axis; the thumb on ring finger activates the physical axis. While the mudras of the left hand activate the frontal energy fields, those of the right, activate the dorsal (back).

The nodal divisions or the sub-lines, dividing each finger into three parts, can be further used to precisely focus on a particular part of the body. For example, in the mental zone, which is from the top of the head to the centre of the throat,

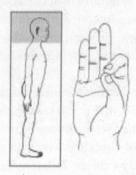

Touching the thumb to the top of the index finger activates the mental axis at the head zone (also called Manomaya Kosthya)

Fig. 2.4 The Hindu Concept of Mudras

the Adam's apple, the first line from the top isolates the forehead, the second line affects the eyes, nose and ears, and the third line relates to the mouth and the throat.

The head is further sub-divided into the mental or thinking part, which is the forehead; it's the emotional part, focused on the ears, eyes and nose—which hear and show our feelings; and the mouth and throat—the physical part, which gives physical expression to our thoughts and emotions.

Similarly, the middle finger and its sub-lines are used for the trunk zone of the body from the throat down to the base of the spine. The first line relates to the chest, the second—up to the navel and the third, below the navel.

The first line on the ring finger covers the portion up to the knees, the second line—from the knees to the ankles, and the third line—from the ankle to the feet.

It is well known that the solar plexus is the centre of the body and the centre of our emotional being. The mental part of the solar plexus manifests itself in our leadership qualities.

The displacement of the energy axis on a particular line of a finger helps us locate the problem area in the body and the type of axis disturbed reveals the dimension and kind of problem—mental, emotional or physical.

There is also a fourth dimension, the psychic zone, represented by the full body, which is measured by the top and sub-lines of the little finger—the first line represents the head or mental faculties, the second line represents the trunk for the emotional faculties, and the third line stands for the legs or physical attributes.

You must have noticed that when people pray, or perform *japa* (say the rosary), they often run the thumb over each finger or place it on the tip and sub-lines of each finger and chant a mantra. In scientific terms, by touching the tip and the sub-lines with the thumb, and concentrating, we provide an energy boost to the corresponding part of the body which helps it remain healthy. If the energy axis of the organ representing that zone is displaced, it regains its alignment by doing so. Acupressure, reflexology and acupuncture work on similar principles by manipulating (pressing or piercing) various nodal points in the body, especially those located on the feet, hands and the ears.

Our home or any other built space can be compared to the human body. It has a centre, like our navel, which is called the *brahmhanabhi*—centre of the space, as well as other sensitive nodes and points which can be energized to improve the energies in the space and, with it, the health and well-being of the occupants.

Effects of Surgery

Today, surgeries are performed at the drop of a hat. We also hear more often than not of surgery or interventions being repeated on the same part of the body more than once—for example, on the sinuses or the heart. When the physical body is opened and closed again surgically, the aura also opens but it does not close, causing ongoing energy leakage from that part of the body. Also, since there is a hole in the aura around that part, the ability of the aura to act as a buffer between the environment and the affected body part is seriously impaired. As a result, recovery is slow and there are recurring problems in the area due to extra vulnerability to bacteria and radiations. Just as a piece of cloth, when stitched after a tear, cannot be as strong as it originally was, and is likely to tear again from the same place, the body too remains susceptible to recurrence of a problem in the part which was subjected to surgery. It is therefore important to fully protect such parts of the body

After conducting numerous experiments, a simple and non-intrusive method has been developed to seal the aura around the part of the body, which has been subjected to surgery. The procedure of correction is described and illustrated on the facing page and can be conducted by people without expert help. The procedure only takes about thirty minutes altogether and requires only a pencil battery/cell.

Post-surgery Healing Exercise

Steps
- Identify the place or the line of surgery/cut.
- Take a small pencil cell/battery.
- First run the positive side of the battery over the surgery/cut in a movement like closing a zip and then take it back to the starting point. Do this twelve times as shown in

the following figure, and then make a cross over the surgery mark (as shown).

Surgery line/cut

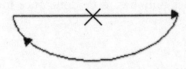

(The battery need not touch the body; it can be a little away from the body. The positive (+) and negative (−) sides are written/marked on the battery.)

- Next, repeat the same zipping action twelve times with the negative side of the battery.

This exercise should be done for all the three periods of a day, facing different directions, either with eyes closed or open, as specified:

Solar Period: Any time between sunrise to sunset.

Lunar Period: Any time between moon rise to moon set.

Earth Period: When there is no moon or no sun. (For example, on Amavasya, the entire night after the sun and moon set till they rise again is the earth period.)

Example

On a day when:

- Sunrise is at 6.00 a.m. and sunset is at 6.00 p.m., the sun period will be from 6 a.m. to 6 p.m., and the sun exercise can be done any time during this period.
- Moon rise is from 7 p.m. to 7 a.m. the next day, the moon period will be from 7 p.m. to 7 a.m.
- Earth period is between 6 p.m. and 7 p.m., when there is no sun or moon.

(The timings are generally given in the newspaper weather report.)

It is not necessary to do all the exercises for all the three periods in one day. They can be done on different days. Exercises for each period take care of the body energies during that particular period.

This entire set of exercises only has to be done once for one particular surgery.

Note
- The exercise can be done either while standing or while sitting.
- For the person who is in bed and cannot face various directions, the correction can be made in the lying position, once with the eyes closed and once with the eyes open, for all three periods. (This will take care of his energies in that position). Once he is fit and able to stand or sit comfortably, the whole exercise as per the chart should be done.

EXERCISES FOR POST-SURGERY HEALING

Solar Period: From Sunrise to Sunset
The movement is anticlockwise as shown by the numbers.

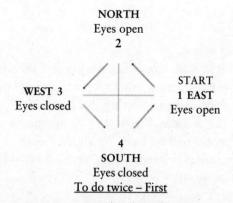

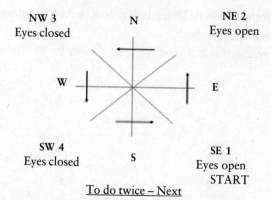

NW 3
Eyes closed

N

NE 2
Eyes open

W

E

SW 4
Eyes closed

S

SE 1
Eyes open
START

<u>To do twice – Next</u>

Lunar Period: From Moon Rise to Moon Set
The movement is clockwise as shown by numbers.

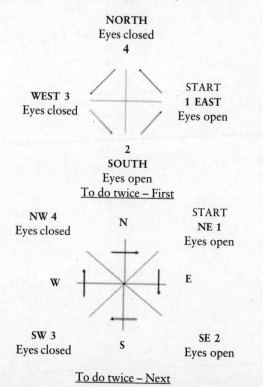

NORTH
Eyes closed
4

WEST 3
Eyes closed

START
1 EAST
Eyes open

2
SOUTH
Eyes open
<u>To do twice – First</u>

NW 4
Eyes closed

N

START
NE 1
Eyes open

W

E

SW 3
Eyes closed

S

SE 2
Eyes open

<u>To do twice – Next</u>

Earth Period: When There Is No Sun or Moon (after Sunset and before Moon rise)

The movement is anticlockwise as shown by the numbers.

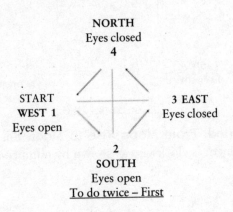

NORTH
Eyes closed
4

START
WEST 1
Eyes open

3 EAST
Eyes closed

2
SOUTH
Eyes open
<u>To do twice – First</u>

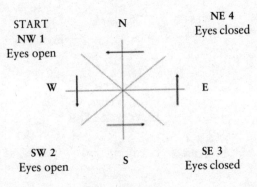

START
NW 1
Eyes open

N

NE 4
Eyes closed

W

E

SW 2
Eyes open

S

SE 3
Eyes closed

<u>To do twice – Next</u>

The movement is clockwise as shown by numbers.

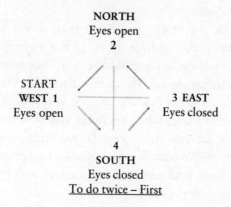

NORTH
Eyes open
2

START
WEST 1
Eyes open

3 EAST
Eyes closed

4
SOUTH
Eyes closed
<u>To do twice – First</u>

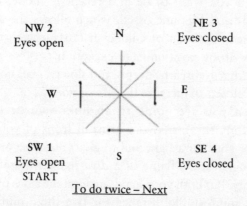

NW 2
Eyes open

N

NE 3
Eyes closed

W

E

SW 1
Eyes open
START

S

SE 4
Eyes closed

<u>To do twice – Next</u>

It is therefore apparent that the understanding of the subtle body and sensitizing ourselves to it is a potent and powerful means of maximizing our potential, performing well, and being healthy and happy.

Do It Yourself
Some simple exercises to keep your aura energized:

1. Stand in a straight position; then move your body clockwise three to four times, in the night period after sunset. Half the circle should be with eyes open, the other half with eyes closed. The motion should be started facing east. This implies that the motion is from east to south, and south to west with eyes open, and west to north, and north to east with eyes closed. Do the same exercise during the day, moving anticlockwise. Start by facing east, turn to the north and west with eyes open, and to the south and east with eyes closed.

2. When you want to be in a receptive mode, keep your hands and legs uncrossed, which allows the aura to be opened. You can of course sit cross-legged; the Indian lotus-sitting position is an exception.

3. Continue to breathe deeply and slowly, occasionally with eyes closed to increase the size of your aura.

4. When you are going to an unknown or unhealthy environment, cross your arms in front of your body to make your aura tight and to give you more protection.

5. A single candle flame or a *diya* flame generates infinite energy. Put both your hands around the sides of the flame at a comfortable distance for two-three minutes, two-three times a day, if possible before sunrise and after sunset. It will energize the body and the aura. Since the hands are connected with all the nodal points of various parts of the body, the energy axes of all parts of the body get aligned by doing this and will stay aligned for a few hours.

6. Yogic exercises and pranayama are very beneficial for the body and for improving the size and quality of the aura.

3

The Eternal Elements

In the blue of the sky,
In the green of the forest,
Whose is the hand
That has painted the glow?
When the winds were asleep
In the womb of the ether,
Who was it that
Roused them and
Bade them to blow?

—Sri Aurobindo

'**E**lementary' refers to something that is easy to learn, know, feel and comprehend.

When we say that a person is in his 'element', we are conveying that he is at his energetic best—witty, happy and active.

Elements are what everything—the earth, the planets, the universe and the human body system—is made up of. They are not separate entities but merge seamlessly into one another. They either nurture and enhance, or destroy and suppress one another depending on the need of the hour.

While we all know that air, water and fire are elements,

not too many of us consider earth to be an element. It seems too solid, tangible and static to be one of the elements, which are perceived to be entities that can be seen and felt, moving and swirling around us.

Since time immemorial, European, Chinese, Indian and Latin American civilizations have recognized the power of the elements and the role they play in creation and existence. They worshipped them, invoked them and used them extensively to create and maintain a better state of health and well-being within the body, in living spaces and surrounding areas.

The Greeks conceived of only four elements. Heraclitus, a revered philosopher, believed that the cosmos was an evolution from and involution into fire out of which air, water and earth evolved. Anaximenes, another learned individual, put air first.

The Chinese spoke about five elements—fire, water, wood, earth and metal.

The Chinese theory of Feng Shui, which means wind and water, is used for town planning and building construction. It studies in great detail, the movement of the five fundamental energies or the five elements which are associated in turn with qualities manifest in the human body—colours, smells, tastes and seasons. They define the progression of these five energies as the Creative Cycle, when they help one another —fire to earth to metal to water to wood and again to fire. Fire forms volcanic layers that crystallize as earth. Earth protects and forms minerals and metals. Metal slabs and layers sustain and create underground water streams. Water helps in growing wood and plants and wood creates fire.

They also talk about the Destructive Cycle in which water douses fire; fire melts metal; metal cuts wood; wood covers the earth; and the earth absorbs water.

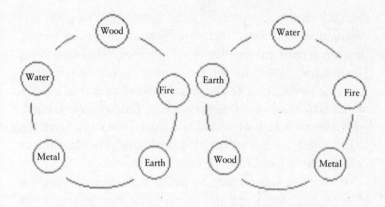

Fig. 3.1 Creative Cycle   Fig. 3.2 Destructive Cycle

The Rig Veda, the ancient Indian treatise on life and creation, written thousands of years ago, spoke about five elements. In addition to the four elements that the Greeks spoke about, the Rig Veda identified a fifth element, Ether, which is all pervasive and owes its origin to cosmic thought and intent. It maintained that not only was ether present in the space inhabited by the earth, other planets, constellations and their surrounding atmosphere, but in all other unknown, undefined and unseen spaces of the universe. We normally assume that the sky (*aakash* or *vyoma*) houses the universe. Thus ether seems to have no substance but can absorb and transmit unlimited amounts of energy and support and hold together the whole universe.

Ether sustains the universal life force energy called *prana* in India, *ki* in Japan, *chi* in China, and so on. Ether creates a vibration that transforms into rhythmic movement and audible sound. We are then led on to the gaseous state—air (*vaayu*), which is unseen but felt and heard, and which touches and caresses us, but is not all pervasive. Air cannot flow through walls, whereas ether can. Fire (*agni*) is the igneous state which introduces us to light, heat, sight, creation and destruction, and form. Light and heat are necessary for the development of animate life. Their absence, according to the Upanishads, causes the *prana* or vital energy to withdraw from the physical frame and retire into the mind and psyche. Water (*jal*) brings taste and a sense of fluidity and stability, with a distinct lack of volatility. Finally, the earth (*prithvi*), is rock solid; it generates myriad smells and provides life and energy with a fixed form in which it can endure.

We see, therefore, that so-called nothingness (space or *shunya*) has energy in equilibrium—that is, it neither emits energy nor is energy deficient. It absorbs energy emitted by the earth and other planets and allows it to reach other planets, for example, sun to earth. Obviously, it requires a medium, which has been named ether, which is fine and all pervasive. The other elements with progressively grosser and denser states are created, activating sensations of touch, heat, sight, taste and smell. The finer the state, the more flexible it is. It can change or transmute and penetrate more easily. The grosser the form, the more static, durable and inflexible it becomes.

The qualities associated with each element are also used metaphorically in our vocabulary too to conjure up images and describe the state we are in. For example, we talk about an *air* of expectancy or foreboding, *fire* in the belly, of a person being down to *earth* or well grounded. We talk about people being in a fluid state of being or existence.

It is universally known that the human body and all forms of creation, including the earth and the planets, consist of all these elements in particular proportions and their variance can cause severe changes and disturbances in our body and the environment. Lack of rainfall can cause drought, excessive dryness, forest fires, excess rainfall/floods, air disturbances such as cyclones or storms . . . we can go on and on. In the body, lack of water, which manifests as thirst or lack of air, vitality or heat can cause severe discomfort and even prove fatal.

The *Panchbhutas*

As per the Indian system, the five elements are known as *Panchbhutas—panch* meaning five and *bhutas* meaning elements. When correctly balanced in the body, they enhance health and well-being. Ancient practices like ayurveda, yoga and t'ai chi, strove to achieve this perfect balance. In fact, we disturb this elemental balance and fall prey to various illnesses because of improper living and eating habits.

Ayurveda has researched the commonly occurring imbalances in people and has classified them into three *prakritis* or types:

1. Excess earth + water = *kapha* (phlegm)
2. Excess fire + air = *pitta* (dryness and skin disorders)
3. Excess air = *vaayu* (digestive and muscular disorders)

Since time immemorial, all medical practitioners have diagnosed the state of health of the body by measuring the pulse rate and more recently, the blood pressure. *Vaids* (Ayurvedic doctors) developed this practice into such a fine art that they were able to diagnose and write prescriptions for the most complex diseases by the nature of the pulse. Even today, we can avoid undergoing complex and expensive tests by pulse diagnosis. If the elements are balanced, the pulse rate, breathing and blood pressure are normal and stamina increases.

Homeopathy, a modern system of medicine, in addition to the pulse, uses comprehensive symptomatic information garnered from the patient. Common queries are: Does the patient like hot or cold drinks, feel excessively hot or cold, like to eat sour or sweet food, have a good appetite, sleep well or not, breathe more from the left or the right nostril, and so on. Answers to these questions help the practitioner to ascertain the balance and proportion of the elements, and the sensory perception of the patient's body.

Homeopathy, which was developed in Germany, also uses a very ancient and effective practice called Potencizing (explained in the previous chapter) to prepare medication. After every potencizing, that is, shaking one drop of germ concentrate with a thousand drops of water, one drop is then added to another thousand drops of water and the same process is repeated, thirty to 200 times. The final product may contain one zillionth of the original, but is thirty to 200 times stronger. This may be difficult to believe, but is based on the same theory of the microchip and the nuclear atom phenomenon—Smaller is Stronger.

During the potencizing, water, air and heat are being extensively charged and balanced to create high, positive and healing energy.

Interrelationship between the Elements, Space, Direction and the Body

'To be at the proper place, facing the proper direction and acting at the right moment, is to be in harmony with the rituals (faith) and efficient in their practice. It is to be in harmony with the universe.'

Ancient scriptures and sciences have dealt extensively with the obvious and intricate relationships between the functions carried out within a space with respect to direction, corresponding elements and parts of the human body, and planets that they relate to.

Ether, which supports creation, naturally represents the whole body and the north-east quadrant of the land/house. In the northern hemisphere, the electro-magnetic energies flow from the north to south because of the polarity, and from east to west, due to the direction in which the earth rotates. Therefore, the north-east quadrant receives the maximum energies and should be the cleanest, most uncluttered part of the house, used for exalted and spiritual activities, for example, the prayer room, the reception in an office, or a bedroom for elderly people.

Air activates change and makes us feel various sensations. It fans fires, generates physical reactions, and mental and emotional responses by what we hear and see because sound is carried by air. It relates to the north-west zone of a house or a plot and the head zone of the human body, which starts from the crown and ends at the Adam's apple on the throat. The head zone has the maximum number of orifices like the ear, nose and mouth, to allow air to get in and out.

Air forms various patterns while travelling and blowing and is also affected by planetary positions, particularly solar and lunar winds. They have a profound effect on the growth of plants and consequently soil erosion and retention (see Fig. 3.3).

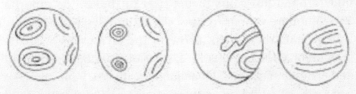

Solar wind patterns during day   Solar wind patterns during night

Fig. 3.3 Solar Wind Patterns

Fire indicates heat and vitality. In a dwelling unit, the kitchen is placed in the south-east or the north-west quadrant, as this is the path of the sun. Creative functions are also done in the south-east, as fire is used to mould and reshape or destroy and recreate objects. Fire and the south-east relate to the leg zone of the body and are synonymous with the sun.

Water relates to the south-west and the stomach portion of the body, in which there is maximum water retention. The south-west is supposed to be the stable zone of the house. People find the co-relation of stability with water a bit of an anachronism. However, looking at it in another way, we see that three-fourths of our planet comprises water, which unless stirred, remains calm and stable. Even after turbulence the water finds its own level. After an earthquake or geological shifts, undulations may take place on the earth and cavities may form, but water remains undisturbed, especially in the sea. Water relates to the moon, and we know that most high tides occur during the moon period. Amazingly the menstrual cycles of most women follow the moon, starting either during the no moon or the full moon day. Ironically, water, which can quench thirst and extinguish fires, is formed by a combination of hydrogen, which generates immense heat, and oxygen, which is essential for burning. A mass or trickle of it also has the tendency to seek out and join other water bodies. Water will either get absorbed by the soil and join underground flows and then a river or the sea, or vaporize and join more vapour to form clouds and descend as rain.

The **earth** supports growth and draws us with its gravitational force so that we can perform various meaningful and creative functions. Huge monuments are built on it; we can walk, sit and sleep on it; we can grow plants, trees, food and flowers. In short, it makes our existence possible. In fact, it is the epicentre of our existence. It has provided us with mountains to climb, valleys to behold, and minerals to sustain our health. Since time immemorial, the centre of a plot of land or a house was considered to be the originating point of the earth's energies within that space, which rose up to meet the cosmic energies and circulate together within the house and its surroundings.

It is found that in situations where the layout of the land or building does not respect the relationship of the elements with their corresponding directions (orientation), there are psychological and mental health problems. These can be rectified by redesigning the layout or, if that is not possible, by placing the elements or their symbols in the proper orientation at a particular height, on the walls or in a niche, in the dwelling unit or workplace.

As illustrated in Table 2.1 (see p. 25), the elements also relate to and are either enhanced or suppressed by certain planets, symbols, musical notes, colours and mantras (hymns). For example, it has been proved that a certain arrangement of musical notes can be played or sung to summon rain or to generate certain effects like creativity and vitality. Different 'VIBGYOR' colours (colours of the rainbow) are used to balance energies and elements in certain parts of the house and for healing various parts of the body. Table 2.1 shows that chakras also relate to elements and different colours can be used to energize them.

Our ancients and many farmers even today can look at the formation of certain lines or streaks in a clear sky, or the halo around the moon and predict that it's going to rain or whether a thunderstorm is round the corner. Such predictions have always been important because they impact their lives and livelihoods.

Like the Chinese system, the Indian system also talks about a creative cycle: ether generates air; air fans fire; fire crystallizes the earth; and the earth supports water. In a destructive cycle, water douses fire; fire destroys the earth; and thus we see that elements never remain static. They need to circulate and move around in order to either enhance or destroy.

When elements do not circulate and stagnate, they cause harmful effects. Water forms algae and attracts dirt when stagnant; air, in a closed environment smells foul; soil needs to be dug, ploughed and watered to build houses and plant seeds which grow into trees and flowers; volcanic fires create geological shifts to destroy and recreate minerals and metals.

Recognizing the importance of the elements in creating, nurturing and sustaining mankind and the universe, it was no wonder that the ancients deified and worshipped them. In south India, the Panchbhoota shrines, a cluster of five temples, are dedicated to Lord Shiva, who represents both creation and destruction, and is worshipped as the embodiment of all five elements. These temples, rich in legend, history, sculptural wealth and traditional practices, have been visited by millions over centuries.

In all ancient forms of prayer, like the Vedic *havan* (ceremony relating to purification by fire), the names of all the elements are chanted and they are offered to the people praying. For example, wood is arranged in a metal container or in a pit dug in the earth and a fire is lit. Water is sprinkled on the earth on the sides of this fire and *samagri* (offering made of rich foods) and wood is put into the fire. The people performing the ceremony chant hymns, evoking peace for the earth and the support and enhancement of the other elements.

BRAHMA is the lord of all creation and thought. He is formless and undefined, and manifest in all creation as ether.

VAAYU, the messenger of Brahma and the other gods, is eulogized in the Rig Veda and other texts but remains formless.

AGNI, the god of creation and destruction, represented in the form of Rudra or SHIVA, is said to wake at dawn when the Sun rises.

VARUNA is described as the god of the ocean. He rules over the waters and is revered by people on the dark day of the moon or the moonless day. He is also invoked for removal of misfortunes. Water, also known as APA, is a life sustainer and a purifier.

EARTH is the mother of all creation. It nurtures and sustains all life and creation. It takes into its womb the form or remains of spent life and creates new life out of it by converting it into minerals or food.

Buddhism is a very ancient spiritual and living system. It is not only widely practised in South Asia and South-East Asia, but is growing roots in the western world. It refers to water, fire, air and the earth as the 'four great essentials', which co-exist and are inseparable from each other.

In the Pali language, a dialect of Sanskrit, spoken by Buddha 2500 years ago, an element is known as *dhatu*— that which bears its own distinct characteristics. The *dhatus* are described as follows:

Earth (*Pathavi*) is translated as 'extension' or 'expansion'. It is a support or foundation for the other elements. It represents qualities of solidity, rigidity and hardness. Depending on the degree of presence of this element, objects are relatively hard or soft.

Water (*Apo*) is 'cohesion' and represents the qualities of liquidity, fluidity, malleability, adaptability or pliability. It flows around solid objects and coheres to them, mirroring their form. It prevents different particles of matter from being scattered about.

Fire (*Tejo*) translates as 'heat' or 'energy' and also 'combustion'. Vivacity, creativity and maturity are the characteristics of this element. Both heat and cold are its properties. The amount of *Tejo* in the atmosphere or in the body determines whether that entity is perceived as hot or cold.

Air (*Vayo*) translates as 'vibration'. All motion, vibration, oscillation and pressure are caused by this element, which is also sometimes referred to as the 'mobile' element.

The Elements as Symbols

Eastern philosophers gave each element its own geometrical symbol, (2D and 3D). The earth is represented by a square or a cube; water by a circle or sphere; fire as a triangle, pyramid or cone; air as a semi-circle, crescent or hemispherical bowl; space or ether as a dot, tiny circle or bead. In addition, thought or consciousness, which creates vibrations and movement, is represented as a thin tail spiralling upwards, like a trail of smoke.

The shape of temples or Buddhist shrines normally represent all the elements. The bottom is in the form of a square after which there is a rounded form, followed by a conical spire topped by a crown containing a crescent and a thin extended rod pointing to the sky and culminating as a point.

The Elements and the Body

The elements are used not only to maintain good health but also to restore lost health. When their balance is restored, it has been repeatedly seen that chronic diseases, which have afflicted people for years, seem to miraculously disappear. This reaffirms the old adage—This body is from nature and nature alone can do the best to it. Let us examine some of the most effective known therapies:

Water Therapy: Water is the most abundant element in our body as 72 per cent of our body is water. Apart from circulating nutrients throughout the body in the form of blood, it also distributes heat. Waste materials which consist of chemicals broken down by the metabolic reactions of the body and processed food are also removed by water. Taking water as an important supplement cures all diseases.

Earth (Food) Therapy: Food is nourishing both for the mind and body. It can keep the body healthy if a variety of foods are consumed in moderate amounts. These should include fruits, vegetables, grains, pulses, seeds, nuts, leaves. All diseases are generated due to the intake of an improper quantity and quality of foods.

Heat Therapy: Heat or fire keeps the body physiologically active. Exercise increases the metabolic rate and consequently the reactions in the body. These in turn improve blood circulation that indirectly helps the removal of toxins and waste materials from the cells. Yoga, which exercises both the mind and body, is now widely accepted as the best form of exercise. Steam, sauna and sun baths are also beneficial.

Air Therapy or Breathing Exercises: We never breathe in a way so that we can fully fill up and utilize the capacity of our lungs. Proper exercise helps us to breathe in and breathe out more air. Pranayama is the most effective breathing exercise which can be done without straining the body. It improves oxygen supply to all the cells of the body and the brain, thus rejuvenating them and enhancing their function. This in turn helps in removal of wastes from the body.

Meditation or Space Therapy: We usually always concentrate on our external body and things around us. Attention is never focused on the interior spaces of our body unless we fall sick. Meditation helps us in connecting with our own being or our inner spaces. This brings wholeness not only to the mind but also to the body.

The flesh, bones, nose and odours are formed from the Earth element. The blood and other liquids in the body, the tongue and taste arise from the Water element. Warmth, skin colouration, the eyes and the shape of the body are formed from the Fire element. The breath, organs of touch and physical sensations are formed from the Air element, while the cavities in the body, the ears and the sounds within the body and those heard by us are enabled by the Space element.

As mentioned earlier, each element relates to a chakra. For example, the Root chakra, located at the base of the spine, is related to earth; Hara, located below the navel, to water; Heart to fire; Throat to air; and the Crown chakra to space or ether.

Panch Mahabhutas	Sense Organs	Sensory Faculty	Properties	Actions
Space	Ears	Hearing	* Creates natural void in the body * No distinct taste	Produces softness, lightness and porosity
Air	Skin	Touch	* Light, clear and dry * Governs inhalation, exhalation, opening and closing of eyelids, extension and contraction of joints, locomotion and other motor functions. * Slightly bitter taste	Creates dryness, lightness and emaciation.
Fire	Eyes	Visual (Sight)	* Rough & bright eyes * Controls temperature and lustre of body colour * Pungent taste	Helps in digestion, maturation, improves eye sight
Earth	Nose	Smell	* Heavy, immobile, compact & rough * Controls organs like teeth, nails, flesh, skin, tendons & muscles * Sweet taste.	* Increases firmness & strength of the body Acts as a nutrient, emollient and purgative
Water	Tongue	Taste	* Cold, heavy fluid * Slimy, fat and sweet by nature * Sweet & astringent, sour & saline taste	* Imparts glossiness * Enhances fluid content & purgative * Acts as nutrient, emollient and purgative

An experiment was conducted with the Lecher Antenna by making a person hold the symbol of a particular element in his hand or by wearing it on his body. It was found that an elemental circuit was formed in the shape of an '8', which started from the Crown chakra and culminated at the Throat, Heart, Hara and Root chakras, respectively.

To summarize and put things in perspective, space is the outcome of the cosmic mind, which creates thought and movement. Vibration creates air, air generates fire, which leads to water, out of which emerges the earth. It therefore becomes obvious that space has only subtle, subjective *prakritis* or characteristics like thought, intellect and ego. From this state are born progressively grosser states like air, fire, water and earth. Earth contains water, fire, air and space; water contains fire, air and space; fire, only air and space; and air, only space.

We have also illustrated that as we progress to each successive element and the grosser states, we add the sense of hearing, touch, taste and smell.

All elements relate to mostly known entities and creations, like planets, colours, symbols, organs and musical notes, which affect us and have a bearing and a profound effect on our life, our body and our environment. Their presence sustains life, their absence causes death. Any disturbance in them causes ill health, which is restored almost immediately and magically by balancing them.

4

The Power of Symbols

The Star
Which leads us to the Promised Land
The Mist
That parts to unveil
A wondrous expanse
The touch which heals
The deepest wounds
The word that promises
A thousand Moons
Symbols, when repeated
Attain awesome power
And lead us kindly
From the unravelled past
To the untrammelled future

How would you define a symbol? The alphabet is a symbol. A word is a symbol. A series of words, used together, or a sentence is a symbol, which signifies a thought, or expresses an emotion. Sketches or pictures are used to convey thoughts or emotions, and a series of these depictions are used to tell a complete story.

Over time, most objects, such as houses, trees, roads,

planets, spaceships, have been given specific symbols which represent them. Repeated use of the symbols results in their becoming firmly embedded in our genetic code, which is passed on to our descendants who take less time to learn them than we did. In fact, often to our surprise, they sometimes seem to be born knowing these symbols!

Symbols activate thoughts and reactions. Our mind consciously or subconsciously through the SIM card of the memory receives a signal and translates it; this activates a response in the mind or body.

Haven't you seen a child who, in spite of not having learnt to read or write formally, still doodles? What does he draw? Shapes of people, a house, a road, a tree, a mountain or shapes that seem unfathomable. How does a child draw a person? He divides the body into three zones—the head, the trunk and the legs. As explained in the chapter on 'Subtle Energies of the Human Body', not only is the body divided into three parts but each part represents different kinds of energy— mental, emotional and physical. Together the whole body represents psychic energy, which connects directly to our intuition and metaphysical reality. It is more powerful than the other energies, because it has finer and more powerful vibrations.

The head zone with the ears signifies inquisitiveness, alertness and the desire to hear and express. The body is much larger to give stability to the head and the leg zone represents agility and movement.

Children can often be found scribbling furiously. What do you think they are doing? Expending excess energy because they have been confined indoors or transcribing thoughts, concepts and images, which we cannot understand and comprehend and they do not have the verbal felicity and logical training to structure and explain?!

Since words, pictures and mathematical formulae are born from thoughts, emotions or inspiration, they are infused with energy—the energy to inspire and generate new ideas and actions.

Children draw concentric squares, circles and triangles again and again. Why do they do so? They energize themselves while creating and looking at them. When others look at them, they too feel happy, elated, inspired or depressed. Positive, creative or happy expressions generate similar reactions and energies that elevate us, whereas negative outpourings cause sorrow, depression and anger, which deplete us.

Symbols: Input vs Output

Symbols are not confined to time: they have unlimited and infinite energy which can be used for as long as people wish to continue to use them and understand their meaning.

Once a meaning has been assigned to a word or a letter, it remains for eternity, like a word written on a piece of paper remains unless erased and rewritten. Of course, it is constantly reinforced by repetition and reiteration. It takes many years to change a thought, a concept or a meaning since the original meaning is well ingrained in our conscious and subconscious mind.

Children are born with genomes in which this historical

learning and understanding is ingrained. They are not yet layered with logic and segmented learning. If they are taught to draw, write and speak a language which their ancestors knew, they would learn it much faster than they would any new language. On the other hand, it is a common syndrome that adults, after a lot of learning, use of intelligence, self-development and attainment of maturity, become cynical, all knowing, bored, narrow minded and intolerant. They lack the enthusiasm and the energy to do more and to learn new things quickly. A current example is how children learn and use computers and the Internet much faster and better than older people.

The story of the microchip: The origins of the microchip can be traced back to the beating of drums in Africa—a manner of communication through sound which could be heard for thousands of miles by all those who wanted to listen, and then reply via their own drum communication in a similar manner. They identified themselves by a particular sound, which would specify their location. This further developed into the Morse code, a communication system using radio frequencies. The microchip is nothing but a series of dots and lines which are identified to mean certain things to hundreds and millions of receivers, who understand them through a software which is universally used. What if this software were to be abandoned or changed? These chips and the devices they run would become redundant and inoperable till the original software is deciphered. We know that a multi-billion dollar nuclear facility can become inoperable and hazardous if the software which interlinks and operates its various facilities becomes corrupted.

Symbols of Faith

Ancient civilizations also relied on symbols. Their microchips were pictures of gods and deities, symbols like the Cross for Christians, '*Om*' and the swastika for Hindus. In all civilizations, each deity was associated with a particular quality or a story. Buddha symbolizes the virtue of renunciation and the need to free ourselves from desire. Christ on a cross represents the power of sacrifice and its ability to inspire generations of people to do good and noble deeds without expecting positive rewards or recognition. Indian and Greek deities represent various virtues and aspirations. Ganesha is a typical example. The elephant head and the trunk represent the ability to assimilate knowledge and wisdom. The single tooth stands for the ability to decide a course of action and not dither. The large ears signify the ability to listen; the big stomach represents the ability to absorb and process thoughts, wisdom and the ability to keep secrets and not divulge them. The carrier or messenger is the mouse, which is small, quick and can get in almost anywhere. It represents mobility.

Durga, the goddess of power, has numerous hands so that she can simultaneously destroy, fight, nurture, create, bless and empower. Hindu mythology has more than 36,000 deities. Each embodies a trait, a virtue, a story or an inspiration. These deities may be real, mythical or symbolic, and have been created by people, to serve a purpose. The deities that are forgotten cease to have meaning and relevance. Brahma, Vishnu (also embodied as Rama and Krishna) and Mahesh (Shiva), are the best known and acknowledged as the Trinity or the Godhead. Brahma is the eternal creator; Vishnu, the preserver and perpetuator, and Shiva, the manifestor of creation (portrayed through the *tandav* dance) and the destroyer, who paves the way for new creation.

The trinity is manifest in many faiths. Christianity believes in the Father who creates, the Son who perpetuates and the Holy Ghost who destroys to pave the way for re-creation.

In Greek mythology, there is a pantheon of deities like Zeus, who holds a book, which represents learning and encourages creation; Apollo, with his bow and arrow, embodies valour; Aphrodite, with well-proportioned contours and a kind and compassionate visage, symbolizes love, compassion and perpetuation. Similar examples are abundant in almost all other civilizations.

Nations eulogize their heroes by installing their statues and portraits in prominent places, celebrating their birthdays and other important milestones.

Images of deities or great men emit positive vibes and good energy because of their good deeds, which have benefitted and inspired people. It is also believed that the energy that we receive from them is amplified manifold if we actively associate with that symbol. A question I have often been asked is, If a person is a Hindu or a Muslim, will the Cross have the same inspiring effect on him? Yes, it would have a positive effect on any person or surrounding, but a Muslim would benefit many times more by the symbol of Allah than by the Cross or the Om because of his higher devotion and reverence to what the symbol of Allah represents. The Muslim is a devout receiver, hence the effect and vibration of this symbol is amplified and, in turn, transmitted as very high energy to others around him via his thoughts, prayers and chanting, since the symbol holds a special meaning for him. A Hindu or a Christian may respect and accept the concept of Allah and Mohammed as a great Prophet, but may not have the same knowledge, reverence and devotion as a Muslim does. Thus, the amplifier effect is far less in extent.

In the Indian subcontinent, the Om and the Swastika are widely used to correct negative energy flows or in more popular parlance, to ward off evil. These symbols have very high energies and are found to work equally well for all. Equivalents of these symbols were used in almost all ancient civilizations. Moreover, these symbols do not represent gods or anything Hindu or Indian. Their meaning and symbolism are universal.

The Egyptian Symbols

The ancient Egyptians used many symbols like the *Djew*—a mountain range which was believed to hold the heavens, and the *Ankhet*, which represented the celestial cycle of sunrise and sunset. The most important symbol was the *Ankh*—a symbol of eternal life. Holding the *Ankh* to the lips symbolized absorbing an offering of breath that would be required in the afterlife.

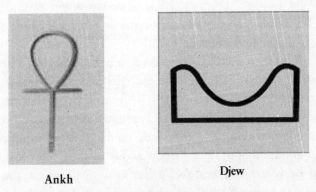

Ankh

Djew

Fig. 4.1 Egyptian Symbols

Yantras

A *yantra* refers to an instrument. It is a geometric design, which operates on the concept that each shape or form emanates energy or a specific frequency and energy pattern. The Pentagon, the Christian Cross, the Swastika, the Pyramid—they are all considered to be *yantras*. *Yantras* are shapes embedded on a particular type of material—copper, brass, silver, cloth, marble, stone, etc., with letters or shapes drawn within them.

One of the most important *yantras* is the Shree Yantra which is a visual representation of the Divine, primarily in the female form. The diagram is a symmetrical figure containing nine interwoven isosceles triangles, five pointing downwards and four upwards. The former represent the female principle of energy or Shakti, which is considered to be dynamic, while the latter corresponds to the static male energy of the *linga* or Shiva. This basic form is surrounded by circular and other square arrangements and is considered to be a cosmic representation of creation and assimilation. This symbol is important because it represents both static and dynamic energies.

Yantras are still used to maintain good health, ward off evil and create wealth. The ancients knew and understood the importance of using the exact proportions and representations. They were energized and consecrated to empower them. The user was made to wear a *yantra* at an anointed hour on a particular day by a person considered to be worthy of bestowing the same. Moreover, the user was supposed to clean the *yantra* and handle it with great reverence. These practices have been dispensed with now.

Many *yantras* available today are found to emit low or even negative energies. This happens perhaps because the proportions of the shapes and the symbols and the purity of the material are not maintained as these symbols are mass produced and not empowered. It is therefore recommended that in current times the use of *yantras* should be avoided except for universal symbols like the Om, Swastika, Allah, the Cross, petals, eight-sided stars, and other basic forms and shapes used individually and not in combination or conjunction with one another, and, of course, drawn in the correct proportions. They should also be cleaned regularly. Even an Om can begin to generate negative energy. Sounds preposterous, doesn't it? Allow me to explain. After many days and months, after the Cross and the Om have absorbed negative energies to their limit, in some rare cases, they can start emitting these very energies. Of course, even normal washing cleanses them.

Measuring Energy

Bovis, a scientist, recognized the effect of subtle energies and started measuring them in units, as mentioned earlier. These energies can be measured on a Bovis scale with a pendulum, with a Lecher Antenna or electromagnetic energy meters. Scientific experiments have shown that 'Om' has possibly the highest energy level of one million Bovis; the Swastika, 4,00,000; the Cross, 1,60,000, and Allah, 1,10,000. These, of course, can be and do get amplified many times more, and can show higher or lower energies at different times and at different locations.

When writing, the ancient forms and proportions of these symbols must be strictly followed for them to be effective.

The following figure shows the correct and incorrect ways of depicting the Swastika.

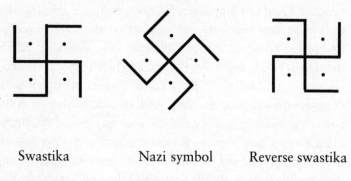

Swastika   Nazi symbol   Reverse swastika

Fig. 4.2 The Swastika

In the case of the cross, the proportion of the length and the width of the members and the point at which they intersect [one-third from the top], is important. The Swastika must always be drawn clockwise and with the members being horizontal and vertical. The anti-clockwise Swastika has a high negative energy. The inclined Swastika (the Nazi symbol) has a very low energy level.

The Swastika

The Swastika was not particular to only Hindu civilizations. Archaeological findings have found evidence of the Swastika in ancient Rome, excavated Grecian cities, Buddhist images, and on Chinese coins dating as far back as 315 BC. Cliff dwellers of Mexico and other parts of Central America considered the Swastika to be a charm to counter evil and to bring good luck, long life and prosperity. The Swastika bears similarities with the four Ls of the Roman alphabet, which stand for Luck, Light, Love and Life; it also resembles the four Gs of the Greek alphabet, the Gammas, the highest forms of energy; and the four Ds, Daleths, of the Hebrew alphabet. In many parts of Europe one can still see old buildings and decorations adorned with the Swastika.

The Cross

The Cross also has a pre-Christian history. In Scandinavia the Tau Cross symbolizes the hammer of the god Thor. In Babylon the Cross with a crescent moon was a symbol of their moon deity. In Hinduism the vertical shift represents the highest celestial state and the horizontal represents the lower earthly state. In Egypt the Ankh Cross is associated with Maat, the goddess of truth.

Fig. 4.3 The Cross

It has been established quite conclusively that the energy axes of people and energies in their surroundings can be aligned and enhanced by chanting or writing the names of these symbols or by wearing them on the body.

These symbols were once also tattooed on certain parts of people's bodies to provide permanent protection. They helped in keeping the energy axis of the body in position, irrespective of the energies of the space which a person occupied and his orientation. The tattoo had the same effect as wearing the symbol.

Spirals

The spiral is an eternal symbol used in all civilizations to depict infinite energy. From the shrine of the temple of Acropolis in Athens, to parts of Peru, where huge spirals on the earth's surface have been seen and photographed by satellites orbiting in outer space; to conch shells which also represent a spiral, and a 20 cm long and wide copper piece with a spiral drawn on it, all kinds of spirals can create strong, positive energy flows. They can change and re-orient negative and divergent energy flows in the surroundings, if correctly used.

When a spiral is drawn, it circulates a high level and infinite energy since it can go on being drawn almost up to infinity. It must be noted that positive energy flows clockwise in the northern hemisphere and anticlockwise in the southern hemisphere. The spiral used must therefore respect this phenomenon. It must move clockwise from the centre in the northern hemisphere and anticlockwise in the southern hemisphere.

We often use this symbol to correct the flow of energy and to balance negative effects when the magnetic gridlines of the earth bisect living or working spaces. Spirals can also correct the ill effects of underground water streams below these spaces, and electrical radiations. They can create virtual openings and heights to enhance energy flows.

In order to conceptualize how a spiral works, imagine a coiled spring. However hard we try to twist the coiled spring in the opposite direction, it will come back to its original position unless we open and straighten it strand by strand. A spring is finite in length, whereas the drawn spiral, as a symbol of energy, springs clockwise infinitely, and has the power to change the energy flows in its vicinity quite easily and firmly.

As described later in the chapter entitled 'The Earth—Our Mother', large towers or rock formations called Dolmens were built on the nodes (intersection points of magnetic gridlines) to nullify their effects. One Dolmen would do the needful for a radius of almost 18 km.

Other Symbols

Symbols like the *rangoli*, which is a decorative depiction used in front of houses or in courtyards to welcome guests, almost universally evokes a feeling of joy.

Sri Aurobindo Ghosh's symbol is the eight-sided star, superimposed with a smaller square, while that of the Mother is a circle with petals. Sri Aurobindo's symbol harnesses cosmic power which provides inspiration, whereas the Mother's symbol brings forth the Earth's protection. Both symbols are often used on the entrances of houses as well as within inner spaces.

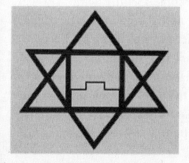

Sri Aurobindo's symbol

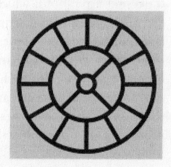

The Mother's symbol

Fig. 4.4 Other Symbols

Case Study: A Party Game

There is a popular party game in which I ask people to draw different images—a Swastika, a flower, a tangled web and a Nazi symbol, and hold the symbols in their hands while standing facing a wall. A person holding the Swastika or the flower, invariably finds that his body is stable and the weight of his body is equally divided between the soles and the toes of his feet. On the other hand, a person holding a tangled web or the Nazi symbol will be found to be unstable and disoriented. Once, a person holding the anticlockwise Swastika was thrown off balance completely and fell down!

Another way of checking the effect of symbols and objects on people is to read their pulse rate before and while they hold a symbol or an object. A lower pulse rate indicates better body comfort, whereas a higher rate denotes discomfort or agitation.

National Flags

National flags of various countries represent certain national traits and aspirations, which people identify with. The US flag showing stars and stripes and the colours blue, white and red, symbolizes valour, victory and unity in diversity, respectively The Indian national flag has three colours, in even proportions, drawn horizontally. Saffron represents spiritual unity in diversity, and the spirit of renunciation and sharing. White represents purity and green represents prosperity and agricultural abundance—the mainstay of India's economy.

Symbols: Powerful Transmitters and Receivers

As amply illustrated in the chapter 'The Sun, Moon and Other Planets', the symbol of a planet held in the hand of a person helps determine the position of the planet in his or her body. As explained, there is a classic position of planets around the feet (geocentric or earth) and above the head (heliocentric or cosmic), which, if disturbed, can cause health and other disorders. This chapter further explains that these disorders can be rectified by the simple use of certain symbols. However, the startling revelation is that although the symbols of the planets used are not known to 99.99 per cent of the population, they still have a beneficial impact. They seem to relate to them. How does this happen? The answer quite simply is that this knowledge or memory has been genetically encoded in us through generations, further illustrating the power of unconscious knowledge, which also manifests as intuition or déjà vu.

In modern drawings in architecture, structural engineering, machine building and process engineering, no words are used. Everything is depicted by symbols, which are widely used and commonly understood. Doors, windows, WCs, staircases, columns, beams, electrical transformers, thermal flows, fluid transmission and thousands of other inputs/aspects are depicted symbolically.

As such, architectural drawings of living and workspaces, and even of townships and cities can be used to map and measure energy flows and levels in these areas. This is done by marking the cardinal directions on the drawings, clearly mentioning the name of the establishment or individual with the full address. This enables experts to map energy flows at a place before actually going there. Of course, since the plan or map does not show details of objects, furniture and utility placements and their relative heights, the actual energies on the site could be impacted or altered. However the location of magnetic gridlines and some other energies emanating from the earth can be fairly accurately located by using the drawings.

Photographs

Similarly, photographs of people can be used to determine their state of health and to check whether their energy body is negative or positive, even though the person may be thousands of miles away. In fact, this is possible even though the photograph may be from his childhood, say when he was five, whereas he is now fifty years old. What actually happens is that the unique frequencies of a person, which can travel millions of miles, connect with each and every photograph of that person, which, in turn, is tuned to receive that particular frequency or energy transmission all the time. It is like a TV programme beamed by a channel being received by all those satellite dishes that have subscribed to that channel, and which are tuned in to receive the signals from the main channel.

Experiments have been conducted where the photograph of a person living in the UK has been checked in India. It showed negative radiations. Over the telephone he was asked to remove a ring that he was wearing. When he confirmed he had done so, the photograph was checked again and was found to be radiating positively. In another example, a person in Mumbai was called from Delhi after his photo tested negative. He was found to be facing west in space and was therefore oriented wrongly, vis-à-vis the earth's energies. As soon as he changed his orientation, the radiation in his photo changed.

The CEO of a multinational company, who is a good

friend of mine, once asked me to test photographs of prospective employees since the number of applicants was very large and he wanted people with good energies and positive attitudes to be considered.

Thus beliefs in practices like voodoo, which involves, for example, piercing a puppet with a pin at a particular part of the body to cause pain to a person who is far away in the same part of his/her body, may not be entirely superstitious. However what can be done to ward off such possibilities is to create protection for oneself by wearing positive and protective symbols or practising energy-strengthening methods like yoga, meditation, reiki and prayer.

Conclusion

Amazing results have been and can be achieved by using and relating to both ancient and modern symbols with caution and understanding. They have the power to move men, machines and mountains. They help us achieve the unattainable and harness the power that they bestowed generations with. We are today creating very powerful symbols, using simple materials and concepts, which are changing and reshaping our worlds and the way future generations will work and think. We would be able to achieve much higher states of being and better results if we also use the symbols, which our ancestors have bequeathed to us, after investing them with our own devotion, power and ingenuity.

The symbols in the sky can change your destiny,
The symbols that you create can change the universe.

5

The World of Colours

In the beginning was the sacred darkness,
Out of which came light,
The light and darkness danced the dance of creation
And the colours of Spectrum were born . . .

—Theo Gimbel

Colour is a part of our daily existence. Colours have been interwoven into the fabric of our life in such a way that it is impossible to visualize our existence without it. Colours affect us—our minds and our moods. How we feel, what we wear, how we decorate our interiors, what we want to express, the things that we associate ourselves with—even without our conscious recognition—are a manifestation of the colours that we choose. In fact, it would be correct to say that colours exert not only physical but emotional, mental and psychological influence over us. They make us feel warm and cool, happy and sad, elated and depressed, energized and depleted. 'Feeling off colour', and 'show your true colours' are phrases that we often hear. To put it simply, colours are the way in which we see the world.

If there were no colours some people believe that we would see only streaks and lines! However, even to see 'streaks and lines', we need to see black and white, which are also colours. Thus without colours, our faculty of sight would hold no meaning!

How Do We See Colours?

The law of nature is such that where there is light there is colour. When light reflects off the surface of an object we perceive colour. When we see a particular colour, say red, what actually happens is that the surface or the space which looks red is absorbing all the other colours present in that environment and reflecting back red.

The obvious question that arises is, what happens to those who cannot see colours at all or correctly, that is, those who are blind or colour-blind? Do colours have the same effect on them as on those who can see? The answer is Yes! This is because their other sensory perceptions like hearing, smelling, feeling temperature changes and vibrations are more heightened than in those with normal eyesight, as colours are energy radiations which stimulate the above sensations.

The colours that we visualize when we close our eyes, the kaleidoscopes which are formed during meditation, are infinitely more beautiful than what we really see. I therefore envy and not pity those who cannot see. Their world is certainly more beautiful than ours.

Colour: a Form of Energy

White light comprises seven main colours known as a colour spectrum (VIBGYOR). This phenomenon was accidentally discovered by Isaac Newton. His experiments showed that light or energy travels in waves. When these waves penetrate a prism of refracting surface, each one is refracted at a different angle and we see a spectrum of seven colours.

Each wave has a length which is known as the wavelength. The waves travel at a certain speed which can be measured in seconds or milliseconds. The number of times the waves are repeated per second or per minute is the frequency of that wave. Any radiation or energy can be characterized by a wavelength or frequency.

When we throw a pebble into a pond it causes ripples that seem to travel on all sides and die down or become less pronounced as we go away from the source of the disturbance or activation. The distance between the crests or the troughs of two waves is the wavelength and the number of waves created per minute is the frequency.

The higher the wavelength, the lesser is the frequency of a particular wave.

The reason why a higher wavelength has a lesser frequency is the same reason why you have to walk or run slower when you take longer strides.

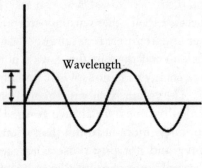

Fig. 5.1 Frequency of Waves Per Minute

The colour that has the longest wavelength and the lowest frequency is red, and the one with the shortest wavelength and highest frequency is violet, as shown in the following illustration:

Violet Indigo Blue Green Yellow Orange Red
Shortest wavelength------------------------Longest wavelength
Highest frequency----------------------------Lowest frequency

Things appear to be of a particular colour because substances within them absorb certain wavelengths and reflect others. A black surface absorbs all colours, so nothing is reflected back. A white surface, on the other hand, reflects all wavelengths.

Do we really see colours the way they are? The answer is No! The human eye takes in darker colours and makes them lighter. Matter on the other hand, absorbs lighter shades and makes them darker.

We are also taught very early in school how we can mix two colours to generate a third.

Colours and Their Effect

Since colours are radiations of energy, they affect and influence us, whether we see them or not. Different colours stimulate us differently and create different moods. For example, in a small room, white or light colours create an impression of space, while any dark colour tends to create claustrophobia.

Depending on the similarities in their nature and effect, VIBGYOR colours are mainly divided into three categories:

Warm Colours: Red, Orange and **Yellow** are known as warm colours and their attributes are mainly those of heating, expanding and stimulating. They enhance mental faculties and will power, intelligence and courage, and are also said to increase ambition.

Red is the colour of blood. It gives us vitality. When 'we see red', we are referring to anger, which is nothing but a sudden rush of energy.

Orange is the colour of spirituality and sensuality. Sages and saints tend to prefer wearing saffron or orange robes. Many religious places are adorned with saffron flags and hangings.

Yellow is the colour of merriment, light-heartedness, freshness, fame, fortune and pure energy, since it is the colour of the sun. It is a colour most liked by children, followed by red, green and blue.

Neutral Colours: Green is a neutral colour and is restful for the eyes. The main attribute of this colour is harmony and it helps keep the mind peaceful and happy. Green is also used as a cleansing colour. Green leaves absorb carbon dioxide and generate oxygen, which is so vital for our health. Hospital walls and medical uniforms are normally green too. Green is also seen to increase interest in religious rituals. It is also looked upon as the colour of prosperity.

Many communities in India use this colour at the time of marriage, for the bridal dress; married women are also supposed to wear green bangles all the time.

Cool Colours: Blue, Indigo and **Violet** are 'cool' colours and usually have a soothing effect on the mind. These colours remove anxiety and bring peace of mind. Cool colours help in spiritual development and meditation, inspiring devotion and faith, and pursuit of truth and higher aspirations.

Blue has a stabilizing effect and helps digestion and cohesiveness.

Indigo helps to develop an intuitive ability and makes it possible to delve into a deeper consciousness.

Violet, of course, is regarded as the colour of the highest aspiration and the universe. It helps during meditation, developing peace and self-empowerment.

Colours and Health

The inability of the body to absorb, process or retain the required quantities of a particular colour, or energy radiation, causes a deficiency in the body that leads to the weakening of the immune system, consequently leading to a health imbalance.

Our wardrobe may be full of fifty sets of clothes, but we tend to wear, say, blue or grey at a given time, or orange and red at other times. Why? Because the colours we like or give preference to over others are the ones in which our body is normally most deficient at that point of time. We subconsciously cater to our body's demand for energy that can be obtained from certain frequencies or colours by wearing them, turning towards them or facing them.

Since time immemorial, this phenomenon has been understood, diagnosed and addressed by developing various colour therapies: wearing clothes of certain colours, which normally are the colours that we like, wearing stones of particular colours, eating food of different colours on different days, use of coloured crystals, and projection of light of various colours on the body. In addition, application of oils and perfumes of various colours is a therapeutic treatment for certain ailments and for enhancing and elevating moods and health conditions. Visualization of coloured light during meditation is common. Many ancient healing systems, like pranic healing, now rediscovered by Master Choa Kok Sui, a successful businessman-turned-healer from the Philippines, also use visualization and mental projections of colours on patients for curing complex health disorders.

While many of these interventions are practised by some individuals and organizations, they have not yet been made mainstream—medical practitioners have not yet started understanding or using these therapies. Not much visible and serious effort has been made to establish the scientific efficacy of these interventions so far. Moreover, it becomes difficult for the lay person to undergo these therapies in a convenient manner. If the person is travelling the therapies may tend to get interrupted. Also, it may not be feasible to carry oils or keep coloured water bottles in the sun if one is travelling.

Colour Radiation Patterns

During experiments conducted by Dr Prabhat Poddar and some others on various conventional therapies, it was found that while a particular colour helped in improving a person's condition, say, for a stomach disorder or pain, during the day, the same colour seemed to have no effect at night. This leads us to the phenomenon described in the chapter on subtle energies where we mentioned that the body assumes a certain set of energy axes during the Sun, the Moon and the Earth periods, repectively, which disappear, almost instantly and magically, at sunset, moon set and in case of the earth period at sunrise and moon rise.

It was similarly found that the colours are arranged from top to bottom of the energy body differently during different periods. Violet is placed at the head and red at the coccyx/base of the spine, in front of the body and vice versa at the back of the body, during the moon and the earth periods, respectively. During the sun period, red is placed at the head and violet below, in front, and vice versa at the back.

This understanding is an important breakthrough for using colour therapy more effectively.

It was also observed that in case of a colour deficiency, the ideal arrangement of colours gets disturbed or re-aligned. The deficiency normally occurs at a particular part of the body, for example, the throat or the solar plexus, which becomes more susceptible to disease. Since that part cannot retain the desired colour, other colours tend to take that position and thus the entire colour arrangement of the body gets displaced or re-aligned.

The challenge, therefore, has been to make this therapy user-friendly and effective, by gathering clinical data and creating scientific validation.

Use of Colour Slides

Dr Prabhat Poddar introduced me to two different sets of colour slides of the vibgyor colours, which were developed for the sun and moon periods, respectively. The sun slides were brighter whereas the moon or earth shades were softer.

Using the Lecher Antenna he proved that with these colour slides the arrangement of colours in a body during the sun, the moon and the earth period could be checked and if the classical order was disturbed, the same could be restored by holding the colours in the left palm for the front of the body and in the right palm for the back of the body in the correct sequence one after the other, each slide being held for one minute.

During his talks, an interesting exercise which he carried out with volunteers from the audience was to ask the volunteer to arrange the seven slides in order of preference or liking, and then scan the body with each colour to find out where the colour was located in the body. It was invariably found that the colours were arranged from head to toe in the same order as the person had arranged the slides.

My colleagues and I have taken this research further. We discovered that while the colour arrangement was corrected by following the method described above, it quickly got disturbed again. It was therefore important to find a way to remove the deficiency permanently. The set of slides now developed by us has been tested for the exact frequency or wavelength of each colour and a powerful symbol has been imprinted on it to enhance its transmission capacity and power. People are tested, their colour deficiency is located and they are given slides for correcting those deficiencies. These can be carried and used easily to remove the deficiency. Normally, a month of regular use (five to ten minutes for each period every day) is sufficient to achieve the desired results. Effects have varied from mildly effective to dramatic. Chronic conditions have also been cured or relieved. After the deficiency has varied removed, the slides can be put in the palms in chronological order to restore the colour balance.

I have been using colour slides to alleviate a serious sinus condition aggravated by a severely deviated septum (nose), for which all doctors have prescribed surgery. Even though it is not corrected and cured fully yet, I am certain that the condition will be cured without surgery.

These slides can also be used for specific parts of the body for curing specific ailments. Certain colours are used on various parts of the body. As elaborated earlier, the warmer ones, like red, orange and yellow are related mostly to the lower part of the body, including the stomach, liver, spleen, kidneys and intestines; they are known to improve blood circulation and keep the muscles healthy.

Green helps in cleansing and maintaining the body's balance; it vitalizes the mind and body, strengthens the nerve centres and brain, purifies the blood, and expels foreign matter and toxins from the body.

The cool colours, namely blue, indigo and violet, affect the mouth, throat and brain; they cure burning sensations of any kind, remove swelling caused by wind within the system. Blue is often used to treat the liver, kidneys and diarrhoea. Indigo is used for treating hormonal imbalances; it is also useful in the healing of cuts and scars. Many of us may recall the widespread use of tincture iodine during our childhood for cuts and bruises. Violet is projected on the pancreas and the adrenal glands.

Effect of Colour Deficiency on the Body's Immunity

It is found that when a colour slide is put in front of a deficiency zone, there is a surge of energy which results in a sudden increase in the pulse rate and blood pressure. After the deficiency is removed, the pulse rate and the blood pressure normally stabilize at a lower level as compared to the previous normal pulse rate and blood pressure. This fact, of course, has to be verified conclusively by clinical trials in hospitals conducted by medical practitioners on different patients in different environments. These trials have already begun. The initial results are encouraging. The deficiency can be checked by the Lecher Antenna or any other dowser like a pendulum. The colour slide is moved from the top of the body to the bottom. Wherever it is absorbed or resonates with the body, the dowser moves forward or clockwise. When there is dissonance or deficiency, it moves backwards or anticlockwise.

The question then is, what does removal of deficiency do for us? It restores the energy balance of the body and increases its immunity to disease.

Colour and Personality

People are often slotted, classified and judged by not only what and how they are wearing their clothes, but by what colour they are wearing and how they carry it. Men are led to believe that they must wear dull and sober colours like greys and browns to look formal and dignified. More often than not, they are dull and predictable. Businessmen, bureaucrats and politicians used to follow and advocate this. Thankfully, things are changing. A Bill Clinton and even a Tony Blair can carry off a red or a parrot green shirt with élan. Artists and musicians can wear the most outlandish colours and look and feel happy. On a particular day, we may feel like wearing a colour combination which is unconventional. Go with it. The willingness to experiment and listen to one's instincts shows mental flexibility and openness to adapt. Criminals wear black, even during the day, which normal people do not. The reason is obvious: their dark deeds deplete their energies. Black helps them to absorb more energy to enable them to carry on.

People tend to wear darker colours and shades at night since the atmospheric energies are low and more absorption is needed.

Colour and Our Built Environment

Colours are an intrinsic part of our built environment and are used by architects and designers all over the world to create different effects in buildings and spaces. The wonderful array of colours portrayed in stained glass windows goes back as far as the sixth century. Colours can make an atmosphere both stimulating and relaxing, and if not used correctly, oppressive and intimidating.

Buildings are coloured externally to show the purpose for which they are used or the aspirations they strive to fulfil. Churches and temples are white or pink to represent purity.

A school may have a white, light blue or a red roof. A playhouse can have a profusion of colours which may represent the whole spectrum—red for vitality and energy, orange and violet within the classrooms for creativity and mental development, indigo for intuition, yellow and pink for brightness and a soothing effect, blue for stability and green for cleansing. The choice of colour also depends on the surroundings—the foreground, the background and the colour of the earth or the base. If we have a clear horizon, we would not use white or grey but would prefer bright and heavier shades. If the earth is bare and brown, or if there is a mountain or a slope behind, we may use white, grey, or lighter shades of green.

We also see and vividly experience how the colour of the earth, the trees, the sky—our entire world, and with them, our moods, change with changes in seasons and the weather.

Colours and Their Effect on Spaces

It is apparent that one does not choose colours only for their appeal as colours. The choice must relate to the surroundings, lighting conditions, size of the building, climatic conditions and the psychological effects which these colours produce.

In a small room, lighter colours are used to create a feeling of space. Dark colours would make the space look even smaller. Colours also appear different under different lighting conditions. Dark shades look lighter in larger, well-lit rooms, while pastels look pale under artificial lights. Also, care has to be taken in the choice of colours to be used together. For example, yellow appears cool against dark brown but appears warmer against green (see colour insert 'Colour Pattern in a Room').

In the old Gothic architecture of churches, Indian *havelis* and palaces, one finds large windows with round or egg-shaped glass panels in all the VIBGYOR colours which are shaped like the aura of the human body, and which create zones of high energy beneficial for the people within. At the altar of a church, for instance, all the energy radiations from the different coloured window panes are made to coalesce to create a high energy zone.

Colour and Orientation

While testing the relation of direction or orientation within a space with colours, and using the Lecher Antenna, it was found that the VIBGYOR range was spread in the south-east and the north-west quadrants and seemed to follow the movement of the sun from sunrise in the east/south-east, to sunset in the west/north-west, and the moving spectrum was egg shaped (see colour insert).

As described in detail earlier, colours can heal people by restoring the disturbed alignment of the human energy axes and removing deficiencies.

Similarly, in homes, specific colours placed in their correct orientation/direction can harmonize negative energies within that space. After various experiments, we learnt that colours are required to be placed during the day and night in the eight cardinal directions (see colour insert 'Indian Colour Orientation during Day and Night').

Thus, by placing a specific colour in a specific direction, we can enhance the energies of our homes and offices. The colour provided could be as small as a dot or size of a bindi. One can also achieve the same effect by putting up a painting in the colour needed, or that is beneficial, in that direction.

Colours applicable for day and night, are active during their respective times. Therefore, it is necessary to place both the appropriate colours for the day as well as the night in each direction. The correction can be done for the house as a whole or for each room separately. It can be done at any level or height, but care should be taken to find the exact eight directions in the room or built space and mark them on the wall. Methods of carrying out this rectification are illustrated and described at the end of this chapter. User-friendly do-it-yourself kits have been developed by us. These can be used by people in their own homes without outside expert help. In fact, people should treat the process like a party game and enjoy themselves.

Colours as Harmonizers

Colours can also be used to counter, at source, the effects of the various BEM (bio-electro-magnetic) radiations. This is possible because all BEM radiations have corresponding colours, which can then be neutralized by using the colours that harmonize them.

Our study included the disturbing influences of thermic, magnetic and electric energies on the human body. The characteristic and harmonizing colour for each of them was identified (see Tables 5.1 and 5.2).

The most interesting application can be on mobile phones or computers where we can use specially developed dots of green, blue and orange/red to minimize or eliminate their negative radiations.

Table 5.1
Characteristic Colours of Harmful BEM Sources and Their
Harmonizing Colours
(Electric)

Region (BEM Sources)	Characteristic Colour	Harmonizing Colour
Drain Pipes, Chimney, Fireplace	Red	Blue
Electric Circuit	Yellow	Green
Electric Transformer	Light Yellow	Light Green
Quartz of Watch	Yellow	Green

Table 5.2
Characteristic Colours of Harmful BEM Sources and Their
Harmonizing Colours
(Magnetic)

Region (BEM Sources)	Characteristic Colour	Harmonizing Colour
Electric Transformer	Violet	Orange
Electric Circuit Quartz of Watch	Blue	Red

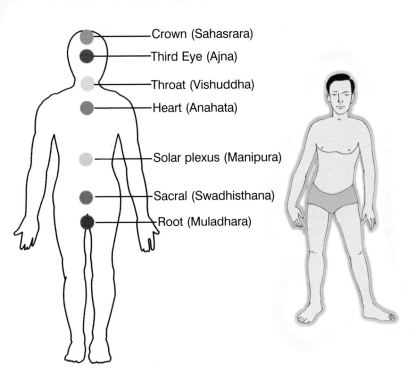

The Chakras
(Refer p. 23)

Auras
(Refer p. 17)

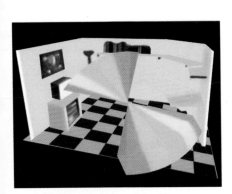

Colour Pattern in a Room
(Refer p. 84)

Auras in Motion
(Refer p. 88)

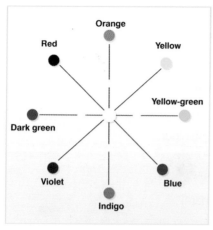

Indian Colour Orientations
during Day
(Refer p. 84)

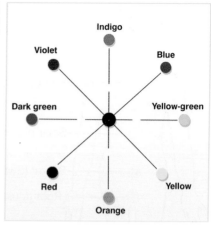

Indian Colour Orientations
at Night
(Refer p. 84)

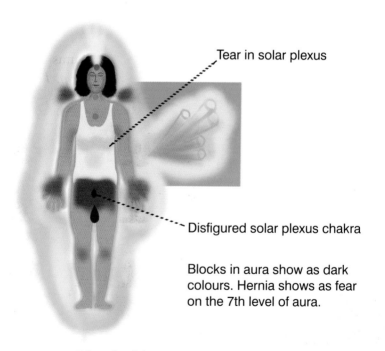

Tear in solar plexus

Disfigured solar plexus chakra

Blocks in aura show as dark
colours. Hernia shows as fear
on the 7th level of aura.

Disturbed Aura
(Refer p. 88)

Colours and Their Corresponding Chakras

Normally, the seven rainbow colours relate to the seven main energy centres or chakras of the body. They are absorbed by these chakras since the wavelength of the chakra corresponds exactly to the wavelength of the colour that it relates to (see colour insert 'Location of Chakras').

Violet/Purple relates to the **Crown** chakra, which is above the head. The related organ of this chakra is the brain and the endocrine gland is the pineal gland. Violet relates to our spiritual awareness.

Indigo relates to the **Brow** chakra or third eye, which is in the centre of the forehead. The related organs of this chakra are the eyes, lower head and sinuses, and the endocrine gland is the pituitary gland. Indigo relates to self-responsibility, that is to say, trusting our own intuition.

Blue relates to the **Throat** chakra. The associated organs of this chakra are the throat and lungs, and the endocrine gland is the thyroid gland. The upper digestive tract can be affected by an imbalance in this area. The throat chakra relates to self-expression.

Green relates to the **Heart** chakra. The associated organs of this chakra are the heart and breasts. The endocrine gland is the thymus gland. Allergies and problems related to the immune system can also be connected with this chakra. This chakra relates to love/self-love.

Yellow relates to the **Solar Plexus** chakra, situated below the ribs. The associated organs are the liver, spleen, stomach and small intestine. The endocrine gland is the pancreas. This chakra relates to self-worth.

Orange relates to the **Sacral** chakra situated in the

abdomen. The organs to which this chakra is related are the uterus, large bowel and prostate. The endocrine glands are the ovaries and testes. This chakra relates to self-respect.

Red relates to the **Base** chakra situated at the base of the spine. The organs to which this chakra is related are the kidneys and bladder. The vertebral column, the hips and legs are also areas related to this chakra. The endocrine gland is the adrenal gland. This chakra relates to self-awareness.

Colours within Auras

The aura, as mentioned earlier, is the visible part of the subtle body. Obviously, in order to be seen, we have to see it in colour. A healthy aura has bright and opalescent colours, ringed with gold. When the aura in the lower part of the body and solar plexus is highly disturbed, it shows a coagulation of a particular colour, which is abnormal (see colour insert 'Disturbed Aura').

Colours do not remain static in an aura, but keep swirling and changing hues every moment, with every thought, every word and every movement.

These images show you the aura around a person's head while performing various acts. The streak of violet emanating from the aura of a person in a musical performance indicates that he is in an exalted state. The passion manifests itself in the colour purple and the green aura surrounding the woman shows that she is energized and happy (see colour insert on 'Auras in Motion').

Colours and Elements

Ether being the finest element, obviously relates to the most profound or elevating colour, violet, which is often the colour of the sky. At other times the sky looks blue, which is the colour for air. Water obviously and apparently is green or green-blue, and fire, red. The earth would be closest to yellow amongst the VIBGYOR colours, or otherwise brown. In the Chinese system, metal is white or aquablue; wood is green; water is blue; fire is red; and the earth, yellow or light brown.

Colours, and Nature

When we think of nature we think of vegetation, foliage, trees, flowers, birds and other creatures.

Flowers are a moment's representation of things that are eternal. They capture all the compassion in the universe and explode into expression in a profusion of space and colours. They have been bestowed on us for our emotional growth, enhancement of our mental faculties and spiritual understanding of nature.

Champa, a flower offered to the gods and worn as an adornment by women, represents psychological perfection. Gulmohur stands for realization. An iris expresses aristocracy of beauty, and a chrysanthemum, life energy. The poppy embodies the spontaneous joy of the cosmos; the tube rose or rajanigandha, new creation; and the hibiscus, dynamic power. According to Sri Aurobindo, colours in flowers and nature represent some of the highest aspirations of mankind. Orange is the colour of the future; yellow—new consciousness; blue—a pure mind; green—life energy, force and growth; pink—loving surrender; and white of integral love for the Divine.

Trees, leaves and foliage are normally coloured various shades of green and are known to absorb carbon dioxide and emit oxygen which gives us life and breath. In summer, the leaves turn to brown and gradually wither away. With the rains the roots absorb more water, and the leaves grow again. In summer, the bacteria are killed by the higher intensity of the sun's rays, thus reducing the necessity of the leaves and foliage for cleansing the environment. Birds and animals are naturally multicoloured and unlike people, do not need clothes to express themselves. A closer study shows that the colours of various animals serve certain biological and physiological needs. Sometimes different colours in different parts of the body are also meant for the same purpose. For example, the digestive portions of an animal or bird's body tend to be darker to absorb more heat, whereas the head zone has a lighter colour to keep the mind cool and protect sensitive parts like the eyes and ears from excessive heat radiation. Animals in colder climates have darker coloured skins or fur coating to withstand the cold and to absorb more heat. Their colours also often change with the seasons. The best example is of a species of wolf found in Antarctica, which has white fur in summer, that turns to dark grey as winter approaches.

Conclusion

We wear, visualize, see, are surrounded by and relate to colours every moment. They mould our lives, enhance our health, give us joy, enhance our personality and liven up our surroundings. They colour what we eat and whet our appetite. They bring radiance to objects that we create or use. They guide, lead and sum up the journey of our lives. Therefore revel in them, live them and love them.

Step-by-step Method To Locate Directions in a Room

Locate the centre (C1) of the room ABCD (see Fig. 5.2).

Place the magnetic compass at the centre Fig. 5.3. With the help of the compass mark the north, south, east and west as well as the north-east, south-east, north-west and south-west directions on the floor (Fig. 5.3).

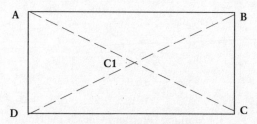

Fig. 5.2 Centre of a Room

Extend these direction lines till the end of the room where the floor joins the wall and mark vertical lines on the wall for that particular direction as shown in Fig. 5.3 (Vertical line NN' for North direction.) Thus we can get all the eight directions marked on the wall. The colours can be placed at any level on that marking and then can be checked with the pendulum or the Lecher Antenna.

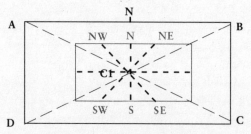

Fig. 5.3 N, S, E & W Directions

This can also be done for the whole house with the help of a plan by locating the centre of the house, then identifying the eight directions from the centre and marking them on the outer walls of the house (Fig. 5.4).

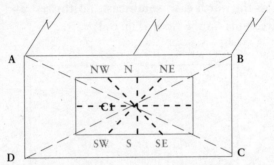

Fig. 5.4 Marking Directions Outside the House

It is of course preferable to do a one-time rectification of the whole house if one has or can get an 'as-built' plan of the house/office. It would be less time consuming and more comprehensive. If a room-by-room rectification is undertaken, certain parts of the house, like the shafts and toilets which are not so accessible, might get left out and will therefore continue to have negative radiations.

6

The Sun, Moon and Other Planets

This is the celestial dance
Of darkness and light,
Furious, beneficial and benign
The stars, planets and the sky
Have the power to govern our lives.

When we are born, the heavens rejoice. The galaxy has one more addition to its family. All the planets and the stars prepare to guide the newborn through the unique and exhilarating journey of life.

The exact date and time of the newborn is noted to the second. The configuration of planets and zodiac signs with respect to the earth is recorded in a visual and descriptive chart called the horoscope. From that horoscope readers can tell which planets and signs will be benevolent to the newborn and which ones will pose problems. They can forecast which periods in the child's future will be good and when great care and caution will be required. Various prescriptions are readied to mitigate the negative impact of the planets. Prayers and rituals are performed; rings, metals, crystals and amulets are recommended for wearing on specific fingers and other parts of the body.

For many people, including me, the horoscope turned into a 'horror-scope'. Often, when things did not seem to be going well, my mother would consult a priest or an astrologer. The 'knowledgeable' man would shake his head in consternation and pronounce that I was in trouble. A, B or C Planet was malefic and not kindly disposed towards me. To alleviate my state, prayers and charity had to be done by or through him. I do not ever remember being told during any period that everything was good and nothing needed to be done.

This led me to the question which has vexed many others too and who do not seem to have got a satisfactory answer. What is the purpose of human endeavour, intellectual thought and positive action, if everything is pre-ordained? To what extent can my will, my aspirations and my consciousness determine how and what I will be?

There are no cut and dried arguments and answers. This chapter is all about what I found out.

Planets and Their Effects

But first the basics. What are planets? They are energy bodies like the earth, made up of elements in varying proportions, which have their own gravitational forces and spin around their own axis as part of the galaxy in different trajectories. Like the organs of the human body, sound, musical notes and colours, they vibrate at specific frequencies which correspond at certain times of the day, month and year with the frequencies of the various organs of the body and other planets to create effects that are beneficial or malefic.

For almost as long as we have known about them, planets have been the subject of intense study and immense curiosity. Their effects on our behaviour, our health and our well-being are constant and profound. Thousands of astronomers and astrologers have spent their entire lifetime unearthing and propounding facts, hypotheses and theories to help people benefit from or avoid the ill-effects of planets. It is now known, years in advance, when a solar or lunar eclipse will occur and in which part of the earth. During this period, the other planet, that is, the sun or the moon, comes between the earth and the moon or the sun, as the case may be. During these periods, the energies and radiations of the planet which is eclipsed do not reach the earth at the desired levels. As a result, harmful germs and bacteria do not get killed. People are advised not to step out as they can be affected by these bacteria. The low energies also result in impaired digestion. It is recommended that people suspend important activities during these periods.

Zodiac Signs or *Raashis*

Imagine a band or a path in the sky, an arc approximately 18 degrees in width, encircling the earth in an east-west direction. Clusters of stars are studded along this belt. Each zodiac sign or *raashi* occupies 30 degrees of this space and is given a name which could be the predominant star, or could denote what the sign represents. Like planets, zodiac signs also have specific vibratory frequencies which resonate with the human body, the earth and the planets.

In the Indian system, the zodiacs are further subdivided into twenty-seven or twenty-eight *nakshatras*, each comprising four subdivisions called *padas* or *charanas*. Thus there are 108 divisions.

Many ancient systems, including the Indian, follow the lunar calendar for all their calculations, including the year. Vedic astrology recognizes only nine planets or *grahas* excluding the earth: the Sun, Moon, Mars, Jupiter, Mercury,

Venus, Saturn, Rahu (ascending node) and Ketu (descending node). Even out of these, the Sun is a star, the Moon a satellite of the earth, and Rahu and Ketu mere mathematical points on the zodiac. However, for the sake of descriptive convenience, we shall refer to them as planets. The lunar system of astrology does not recognize the extra saturnine planets, Uranus, Neptune and Pluto, as planets or *grahas*. The recent disqualification of Pluto as a planet in the solar system as per astrology, is interesting. Who knows, Uranus and Neptune may be the next ones on the chopping block!

Nine planets or *grahas* multiplied by twelve zodiac signs or *raashis*, manifest as 108 situations or *dashas*—permutations and combinations of various possibilities. People often use rosaries with 108 beads, and intone an affirmation or a powerful word 108 times.

Astronomers continue to find out facts about the planets and how to harness their energies for our benefit. Astronauts and scientists have reached a couple of them and positioned satellites on them, which beam millions of megabytes of data for analysis and dissemination. They are now planning to inhabit them.

Astrologers, on the other hand, tell us effective ways to enhance the munificence of the planets in our lives. Like businessmen, craftsmen, scientists and musicians, their knowledge, power of analysis, communication skills and abilities vary. Only a few are very capable. Due to the esoteric nature of the effects of the planets that cannot be easily validated, it is difficult to separate the wheat from the chaff. Many of us spend our lives hobbling from one astrologer to the other, or soothsayers and quacks, in desperate search of quick solutions. More often than not, we end up thoroughly confused with no confidence left in ourselves.

Astronomy

Astronomy is concerned with the observation of the relative motion of the planets, constellations as well as other heavenly bodies, and the detailed mathematical calculations concerning them. The science is as old as time itself. It deals with phenomena like the rotation and revolution of the earth, how seasons are formed, how eclipses occur, the concepts of solar and lunar months and equinoxes. It is used extensively to predict weather patterns and the most appropriate time for planting crops. In our villages even today and in countries like Japan and Cambodia, this knowledge is extensively used in organic farming for planting and harvesting, which corresponds with the relative position of the planets with respect to the earth.

Astronomy is said to have originated in Babylon, now in Iraq, around the fourth millennium BC It then spread to Egypt. The Chinese and the Mayans of Central America and scholars from India were also skilled astronomers.

Astrology

Astrology is based on the theory that particular configurations of the heavenly bodies at one's birth are significantly related to one's personality or character and life events. An individual's horoscope is a geocentric map of the sky, in which are located important elements such as the zodiac signs, planets, the Ascendants and the Houses, and the position each occupies at the time of the individual's birth. Astrology should be looked upon as a guide to the understanding of the laws of the universe that affect the functions and fate of people.

Astrology in India today is the product of migrations that brought about an exchange of information and experience.

The symbolism of the twelve signs of the zodiac which are very important in astrology, does not find its origin in the Vedas but is the product of Greek/Graeco-Roman influence during the time of Vedanga-Jyotisa (A.D. 500) when the first mathematical-based astronomical text, the *Aryabhatiya* appeared. Gradually, the Nakshatra system was replaced by the twelve signs of the zodiacs.

Fig. 6.1 The Astrolabe

Many ancient and modern scientific instruments have been developed and are used to correctly read and map the relative position of planets. One of them that has been used quite extensively in Islamic countries is the Astrolabe. (see Fig. 6.1) which was used to calculate the position of the Sun in relation to the zodiac signs. The path of the Sun, when seen from the Earth, was known to be ecliptical. The ecliptic was devised into twelve equal sections to represent each zodiac sign. The Astrolabe provides a simple method for a non mathematician to calculate and observe the positions and angles of the zodiac signs.

Astrology was also used in medical science to understand

and correct health imbalances in the human body. In Latin America, blood-letting, a medical treatment intended to rectify the imbalance of bodily hormones, was regulated by the position of the moon. Also, every sign of the zodiac was supposed to rule a certain part of the body. For example, it was believed that Sagittarius ruled the thighs, and Pisces, the feet. It was believed that when the moon was in the constellation which ruled the particular part of the body, blood-letting from that part of the body was to be avoided as this could lead to excessive bleeding. The menstrual cycle of women, if undisturbed, follows the lunar cycle of 28 days. It either starts on the full moon or the new moon day. People are also known to behave unnaturally during these days. It has been found that the maximum number of crimes and acts of lunacy are committed on full moon days.

Principles of Indian Astrology
There are, in all, thirteen planets which have an influence on human life:
The Sun, Moon, Mercury, Venus, Earth, Mars, Jupiter, Saturn, Ascending Node (Rahu), Descending Node (Ketu), Uranus, Neptune and Pluto.

As mentioned earlier, the last three planets do not figure as planets in the Indian pantheon.

The twelve signs of the zodiac are: Aries, Taurus, Gemini, Cancer, Leo, Virgo, Libra, Scorpio, Sagittarius, Capricorn, Aquarius and Pisces.

Planetary Characteristics

Different names have been given to the planets by Indian astronomers that indeed seem to be much more appropriate for astrological purposes. Mars is Mangal, the Auspicious,

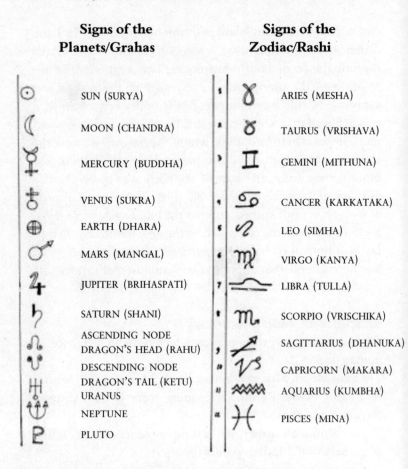

Fig. 6.2 Planets and Zodiac Signs

euphemistically termed so because of its association with great malignancy; Mercury is Buddha, the clever, intellectual god, son of the Moon and Tara, wife of Brihaspati, Prime Minister of Indra, spiritual and political adviser of the gods; Venus is Sukra, who occupies the same position to the Titans as Mercury/Buddha; Saturn is the malevolent Shani, child of the Sun. Rahu and Ketu are the Titans of our mythology.

Except for the last two, all the other Indian names for planets or *grahas* are also the names of the days of the week.

Planets—Masters of the Zodiac Signs

Each zodiac sign or *raashi* is governed by a planet. In Indian astrology each sign has an associated devata, a spiritual being. He is not considered the sign's master, but its protector and the protector of all who are born under that sign.

Sl. No.	Indian God	Western God	Sign of the Zodiac	Raashis/ Zodiac
1.	Indra	Zeus – Odin	Ram	Aries
2.	Agni	Moloch – Thor	Bull	Taurus
3.	Aswins	Castor – Pollux	Twins	Gemini
4.	Upendra	Baal	Crab	Cancer
5.	Varuna	Poseidon	Lion	Leo
6.	Savitri or Sita	Astarte-Aphrodite	Girl	Virgo
7.	Yama	Hades	Balance	Libra
8.	Aryana	Ares	Scorpion	Scorpio
9.	Mitra or Bhava	Apollo-Phoebus	Archer	Sagittarius
10.	Saraswati or Ganga	Nais	Crocodile	Capricorn
11.	Parjanya	Apis	Jar	Aquarius
12.	Nara	Nereus	Fish	Pisces

Table 6.1 Protectors of Zodiac Signs

Effects of the Moon and the Constellations on Agriculture

The ancient practice of farming, in India, was known as *rishikheti* or farming as per the knowledge of the sages, and the contemporary form of bio-dynamic farming, uses a *panchang* or bio-dynamic calendar. This was developed as a result of centuries of observations.

It is widely believed that the moon was thrown out from the Pacific Ocean to orbit around the earth. It acts like a magnifying glass that amplifies the energies of the constellation over which it passes. The twelve constellations form four groups of three or trines. One affects the root of plants; another, the leaf and stem; the third affects the flower; and the fourth, the fruit and seed. When the moon is in front of a constellation which affects the root zone, we should plant vegetables whose roots are consumed, such as carrots and radishes. Spinach and lettuce should be planted when the moon is in front of a leaf constellation, and so on.

The moon, as we all know, orbits around the earth every twenty-eight or twenty-nine days. It ascends during the first fourteen days, which means it moves further and further north till it reaches its apex, which is when it passes between the Gemini twins. Then it starts descending towards the south. The earth is believed to breathe in energies when the moon is descending and breathe out energies when it is ascending. Therefore the best time to do any planting is when the moon is in its descending mode and in front of the appropriate constellation.

The path of the moon around the earth and the path of the earth around the sun intersect. When this takes place, this is a period of negative energy when, other than watering, no agricultural activities are conducted. It is best not to schedule important meetings on that day. When the node falls on a full moon day, there is a lunar eclipse. On a new moon day (no moon is visible), there is a solar eclipse. A special day for agriculture is when the earth is between the moon and Jupiter. On this day, the energies are extremely positive and any agricultural activity can be undertaken.

Planets, Zodiac Signs and Perfumes

Everything in creation has a smell. This characteristic is a measure of the volatility of the substance, or the speed at which it evaporates. Dr Charles Piesse, in his book, published in 1880, called *The Art of Perfumery*, proposed that like music, planets and colours, essences too have a vibratory frequency. Like music, they too correspond to a scale and create harmony. Like a false note, or dissonant smell, they too can ruin the harmony. They have the ability to transpose themselves to a colour or a note. If keynote C is run up the electromagnetic spectrum several thousand degrees, it is visible as red and thousands of degrees down as Rose. Up from the middle C on the fragrance scale, it becomes Camphor; then another octave, Jasmine; then Pineapple. Going down from middle C, we experience Sandalwood, Patchouli. All these can be represented by different shades of the colour red.

Therefore, it seems logical that the effects of certain planets can be created to simulate or enhance the effects of those planets which have the same vibrations. In his book, *Perfume Astrology and You,* Piesse has listed the perfumes corresponding to various planets and zodiac signs. He has also specified the perfumes most appropriate according to the date of birth and the time when they should be applied. He has expanded on the emotional effect of smells. We often talk about smelling danger or fear. Piesse suggests that a growing intellect has weakened our olfactory senses.

After conducting a series of experiments to measure the intensity of the odour, Piesse established that when an alcoholic solution of essences was allowed to evaporate, the most volatile essence evaporated first. He suggested that odours affected the olfactory senses and the brain in direct proportion to their volatility. Thus, low volatility substances like amber and musk release the most powerful odours, followed by cedar wood and patchouli, which possess higher volatility, and finally there are odours with a high degree of volatility like English lavender and citron.

Effect of Gems

Gems, which are translucent crystals and opaque coloured stones, are used extensively in astrology to enhance or nullify the effects of planets. These are usually prescribed by astrologers to be worn on the fingers or around the neck. They shield the wearer with an electromagnetic field which protects him from the negative radiations of planets. The shape, size, purity and the time when a gem is worn for the first time are considered vital. The colour of the gem usually corresponds to the designated colours of various planets (see Table 2.1, page 25).

It must be noted that wearing a gemstone incorrectly can cause immense harm. The subtle body's energy field can get short-circuited by chipped, cracked, or blemished gems, as also by their incorrect shape or size.

Orientation of Gems: Every prismatic stone, for example, a diamond, should be worn with the correct orientation. A fact not known by most wearers and almost all the astrologers who prescribe the size, shape, finger and even where to buy the stone from, is the correct orientation of the gem on the finger with respect to the body. When a stone is set on a ring and worn, a part of the stone is pointing away from the body and a part towards it. If we take it off and turn it so that the directions get reversed, the orientation changes. This is especially true of prismatic stones like diamonds but not important if a round opaque stone like a pearl or coral is worn. This happens because a prism either converges or dissipates light or energy. If worn the wrong way, the body energy is thrown out instead of the cosmic energy being absorbed by the body. It is also important to clean gems with spirit or salt water, against a candle flame or in direct sunlight.

Since each planet and gem emits radiations corresponding to certain colours, they are perceived to be of that particular colour.

Certain gems relate to each of the planets (see Table 2.1 on page 25). The chart shows the co-relation between the seven chakras, colours, etc. as per Vedic astrology (Rahu and Ketu are nodes and are excluded from the seven in the main chart). The gems relating to the Sun and Moon are Ruby and Pearl, respectively. The Bij mantra connected with the Crown chakra is 'Aha' and the Yantra for Sun is 'Spiral' and Moon is 'Crescent' (see Table 2.1, p. 25).

Clarity, Cut and Polish: A gem should be clear and clean. It should not have flaws like inclusions. Inclusions can be air bubbles, fluids, mineral grains. Some such imperfections can be eliminated by heat treatment.

Gem stones are also cut and polished in various shapes and to different degrees of brightness to create certain effects of refraction and reflection. For example, a diamond can have as many as sixty facets or surfaces, to increase the fire or refraction within.

If a gem is well cut and polished, its lustre and brilliance are enhanced. Lustre is due to the light reflected from the surface, whereas brilliance is attributed to the reflection from within.

Lustre and Brilliance: Some stones flash like the sun, while others have a softer subtler lustre. For better lustre, gems must have a smooth surface and should be well polished. Diamonds, of course, have the brightest lustre. The brilliance of a gem is judged by its radiance and its sparkle which is enhanced by its cut. The reflection of light depends on its Refractive Index (RI). The RI measures the movement of the light within the gemstone. Refraction is a phenomenon caused by the changing speed of light, as it moves from air to another medium. The denser the stone, the higher its refractive index.

Hardness, Stability and Toughness: In technical terms, hardness reflects the strength of the chemical bonding within a gem. Mohr's Scale denotes the hardness number from 1(softest) to 10 (hardest). A diamond is the hardest, being 10 on the Mohr's Scale. It is however important to know that the numbers do not represent the proportionate degree of hardness. A corundum (9) is four times softer than a diamond. Gems with a hardness of less than 7 tend to get scratched by quartz which is normally present in dust. Mohr's Scale lists the hardness quotient as: 1 – talc, 2.5 – fingernail, 3 – copper coin, 4 – fluorite, 5 – apatite, 5.5 – glass, 6 – feldspar, 6.5 – steel, 7 – quartz, 8 – topaz, 9 – corundum and 10 – diamond.

Stability is gauged by the effect of chemicals and the outside environment on gems. Pearls can be damaged by alcohol, perfumes and acids; amethysts can fade in sunlight; skin oils discolour porous gems like turquoise; and opals, which contain water, when subjected to dry air, can crack due to loss of original volume.

A gem's toughness is normally reflected by how well it resists cracking, chipping and breaking. Crystals often have a plane of weakness or a cleavage. Ironically, a diamond or a coral, which are 10 and 8, respectively, on Mohr's Scale, is not as tough as a nephrite jade, which has a hardness of 6, and is the toughest stone because of its strong interlocking fibre crystals. The pearl has a hardness of only three. Ironically, a diamond, if dropped, can break, whereas a pearl will not.

Synthetic stones and necklaces are to be strictly avoided as they impede the natural energy flows within, and those from the earth and cosmos to the body. Gems, if correctly prescribed, should be worn on the right hand and metals on the left hand for both genders, the exception being that diamonds can be worn on the left ring finger only by women.

Gold is a metal that can be worn on any part of the body as it has the same wavelength as the cells of the human body.

Gemology

Gemology is a science which not only deals with the cut, polish, shape and size of gems, but with the study of almost all other properties and indices like refractive index, specific gravity, cleavages, hardness and durability. This science is gaining tremendous popularity as the demand and value of gems increases every day.

Some gems are worn according to the person's moods and whims, however, most others are prescribed by astrologers.

It is true that stones correctly prescribed and worn can bring about profound changes in fame and fortune, and can cure illnesses and enhance health. Unfortunately, astrologers who can prescribe them correctly are few and far between.

Other than academic study, a deeper understanding and empathy towards the mental and emotional landscape of the client is crucial. Moreover, there is usually no attempt made to check and validate. What is often suggested is that the person should wear the gem and observe the effect over a week or month. This results in expensive purchases of gems and wearing them without quite knowing the dangerous effects they could have. This is an avoidable practice.

Since we cannot be sure of the astrologer's recommendations and, in any case, they do not specify orientations, is there a way by which we can find out by ourselves? We can. Measure your pulse rate before and ten minutes after holding the stone on the relevant finger. If it reduces after wearing the gem or ring, it should be construed as beneficial. If it goes up, then rotate the stone to change its orientation and recheck. If the pulse rate continues to be high, we can safely conclude that it is not meant for us.

Self-help

Can we get away from all this and help ourselves? Can we relate to and use these planets to benefit ourselves without outside help. The answer is Yes. Let us understand how.

It is now being increasingly accepted that the human body is a microcosm of the universe. Whatever exists outside exists within. The constant interplay between the universe and the human body governs our health and well-being. Foolishly, we hanker for more fame and fortune. When we are born, the position of the planets generates powerful forces, which are received and decoded by the SIM card of our consciousness; signals are sent to various parts of our body and mind. While we cannot change our time of birth and the effects that it creates, we can, by conscious thought, meditation and action, change the program of our SIM card. Consequently, the signals sent to our mind and body can be altered and do not have to be irrevocably preordained.

Doesn't this sound great? How do we begin to make it happen? Constant practice of meditation may not be possible for most of us. As mentioned earlier, wearing of protective symbols can help; correctly orienting ourselves, prayer, salt water baths, cleansing what we wear with a flame can also help. What else?

Another important remedy is to maintain the position of the planets around our bodies. Let me explain how.

As per Vedic astrology, the planetary system is geocentric, that is, the earth is considered to be the centre of cosmic energy. This is contrary to Western astrology which places the sun at the centre of the planetary system. This is called the heliocentric system.

We have already mentioned that the human body is a microcosm of the universe. It can react to all phenomena outside, either positively or negatively.

An interesting experiment was carried out a few years ago. The symbols of the planets were held in the palms of the hand, one at a time, and the body was scanned on both the left and the right side with the Lecher Antenna set at wavelengths to measure cosmic and earth energies. It was discovered that the planets were located at a regular distance on either side of the body around the head and feet, respectively, at a regular spacing.

Heliocentric Energy System

The position of the planets with respect to the head zone of the body—dealing with cosmic energies—has a very interesting

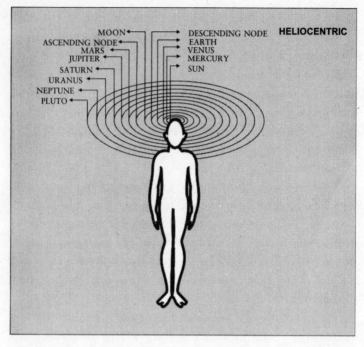

Fig. 6.3 Heliocentric System of the Body with Respect to the Planets

pattern. With the sun at the centre, the planets move around it in a heliocentric layout, reflecting the solar system called Heliocentric Energy System.

Geocentric Energy System

With the feet as the channel, the pattern of the planetary system is based on the fact that the earth is the centre of energy instead of the sun, and the planets are placed around the earth. This configuration, called geocentric, is opposed to the Western understanding of the solar system. It implies that the effects of the planets act in the body through the

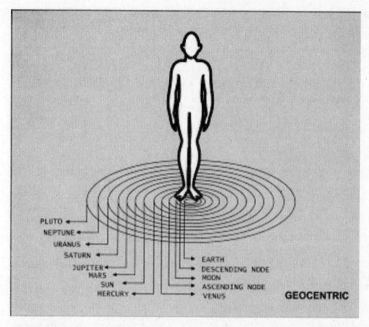

Fig. 6.4 Geocentric System of the Body with Respect to the Planets

earth energies from the feet up, and through the sun as cosmic energies from the head down.

Combined Heliocentric and Geocentric Systems

These polarities—the head and the feet—are the primary channelling points of the cosmic and earth energies into the body. This is where they are gathered, concentrated, and through these polarities, they work and influence the body.

Each part or zone of the body also corresponds to a planet or to a sign of the zodiac, and these together form an interesting relationship or pattern of radiation, as shown in the following illustrations.

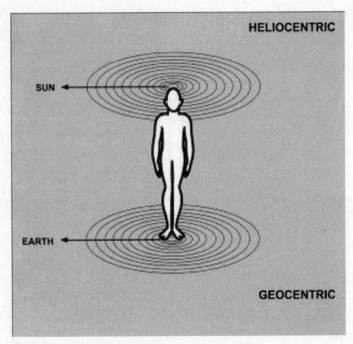

Fig. 6.5 Combination of Heliocentric and Geocentric Systems of the
Body with Respect to the Planets

Perhaps the origin of the stepped pyramid lies in the understanding of this subtle relationship of the human body and planetary system as well as the human body and the signs of the zodiac.

The positions of the planets and the zodiac signs shown in these illustrations are for people who are mentally, emotionally and physically healthy.

However, this arrangement of planets and zodiac signs around the body could get affected both at the head zone and feet zone due to various reasons. Such imbalances can be corrected by using the symbol Om and the Swastika etched

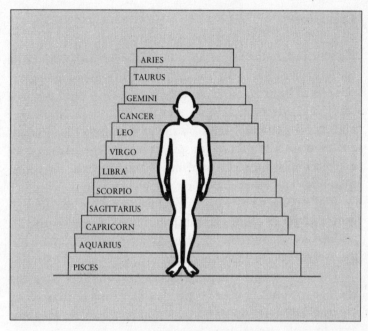

Fig. 6.6 Energy Correction Methods

and painted on thick paper in a specific manner. The symbol Om aligns the cosmic energy planetary system at the head zone positively, while the swastika symbol aligns the earth energy planetary system at the feet zone. Used in reverse, these symbols have no impact. One can also use spirals etched clockwise in the northern hemisphere and anticlockwise in the southern hemisphere above the head and feet, respectively, for similar effects. I am sure that appropriate symbols relating to the Christian, Islamic and other faiths and traditions can be used as effectively.

Conclusion

Planets and zodiac signs have not only ruled the skies and the universe, but with the help of horoscopes and gems prescribed by astrologers, have held sway over our lives. The study and effects of eclipses and the sun, moon and other planets on particular days on the earth on people, animals and plants is a subject of constant thought. These studies are used for improving yields of plants, health of people, predicting calamities and other important events like war.

While it can be a heady experience to bask in the glow of people's faith, practitioners must understand that it also places an onerous responsibility on them to be true to their followers, themselves and to their vocation.

The bad news is that not many practitioners have the courage to admit to their clients that they cannot understand a particular situation or condition and, therefore, may not have the solution to their problems.

The good news is that simple ways are available to empower and help ourselves by using our own body as an antenna or a sensor, hence enabling us to break free from the shackles of wearing gems on our bodies out of fear and superstitions inspired by ill-informed astrologers and gemologists.

7

Significance of Rituals

The world is my oyster
An unending cycle
Of awakening and slumber.
In between
There are many
Things to be done
Rituals to be performed
With diligence and fun
Before you and I
Are truly done.

*A**arti* is the best-known ritual in India. It is performed before starting a new activity, to welcome a person, on entering a new house, and in temples before sunrise and after sunset. People in many households in India still perform the *aarti* before leaving for work in the morning and after returning.

An *aarti* is performed by placing lighted lamps or diyas on a flat vessel, and moving it clockwise in space. The flame is then offered to devotees who place their palms above or on the sides of the flames to absorb the energies emanating from them.

It is now known that the meridians and nodes of various parts of the body are located in the palms and the soles of the feet. By subjecting the palms to this infinite energy source, the energy axis (see Fig. 2.2 on p. 27 in the chapter 'Subtle Energies of the Human Body') becomes properly aligned for many hours and keeps us healthy and active. Variations of the *aarti* are used in almost all cultures where fire is venerated as a great source of life and energy.

Over a period of time each civilization develops its own distinct set of rituals which reflects its aspirations, belief systems, traditions and cultural identity. The older the civilization, the more rituals it is likely to have. Countries in continents like Africa, Asia and South America have innumerable rituals, whereas, Australia and the US, have virtually no rituals except for those of their tribes, which are isolated from the mainstream.

Rituals are increasingly forgotten and ignored, especially in urban societies, whereas they are still remembered and practised in rural areas. In ancient times, rituals and their observance, were based on scientific research and performed for good health, well-being and prosperity. It was difficult to explain the meaning to most of the population who relied on the wisdom of their ancestors and practised them diligently, experiencing the benefits from their observance. Gradually, these rituals became a part of religious practice and perpetuation of family tradition.

In urban societies, both religious practices and family traditions are largely disregarded because of stresses and time constraints, as well as the emergence of the nuclear family system. With different parts of the family located in different cities, and both husband and wife working, children are seldom introduced to family rituals. Grandparents are not around to spend time with their grandchildren to tell them stories. Books are out, video games are in.

However, we find that ethnic communities who have lived together and still maintain close links in alien countries, practise customs and rituals which may have been forgotten in the parent country. Examples abound—there are Chinatowns in India and Europe; Indians in Fiji, Mauritius, Singapore and Madagascar, and so on.

Today rituals are considered superstitious and stupid. We often refer to a person as being 'ritualistic' in a disparaging manner. The problem with rituals is that nobody, including the village elders and our wise grandparents, know or can explain why these rituals are relevant and how they benefit people and societies. Many Greeks and Romans practised rituals without knowing their meaning; they felt that it was a way of remembering their ancestors and keeping links with them, so that they could continue to receive their benevolence and blessings.

Nevertheless, not all rituals are outdated and meaningless. A few will be discussed here and elaborated upon to give us a flavour of their meaning and significance. We will discover that many of these can bring immense benefit to us.

Folding of Hands: In many ancient civilizations, including the Indian, Thai, Japanese, Chinese and Indonesian, the most well-known ritual is that of joining the hands together in front of the body and bowing to greet others, or while praying. This is no coincidence! When the palms are joined, the whole body forms a closed energy loop, in which energies circulate perfectly. Bowing expresses humility and evokes blessings, good feelings and kindness, which flow as positive energies towards us.

Touching of Feet: In India, the ritual of touching a respected or revered person's feet to seek blessings is common. The person so honoured reciprocates by placing his hand on the other's head, thus releasing a total energy flow between both people.

Lighting a Candle: A commonly heard saying is, 'Light a candle and bring happiness to someone's life'. A single flame emits infinite energy. In all traditions, a single candle or lamp or an odd number of them are lit, that is, three, five etc. in candelabras at the altars of churches. This is so because when we light an even number of candles (two, four etc.), a strong laser beam is formed between any two, which not only concentrates all the energy of the two flames within that line, but also draws energy from the rest of that environment to itself, thereby making that area devoid of all energy.

However, this beam of energy can be used for curing an ache, a cut or discomforts by positioning the affected part of the body between two candle flames, which provide concentrated heat and missing vital energy to that part.

During Deepawali, the Indian festival of lights, each home is adorned with many diyas or candles. Many families have heard that it is auspicious to light an odd number of candles but they do not know why!

Thus, while fifty-one candles may provide much more illumination than one, the quantum of energy provided is the same. The candlebra that are available and are used in many homes normally hold three, five or any odd number of candles. It is recommended that a candle is lit in rooms or spaces which have not been used for a long time to dispel negative energies.

Abhishekam: In temples, especially in southern India, another elaborate ritual is performed. This is called *Abhishekam*. It entails the frequent bathing of the deity with a viscous liquid, made up of milk, honey and many other ingredients. The repeated bathing of the deity creates humidity in the atmosphere. This humidity does not allow the liquid on the surface of the deity to evaporate easily, and the excess liquid clings to the surface. This phenomenon is called surface tension, which brings the negative ions within the deity to its surface. Subsequently, when the *aarti* is performed, the heat causes the liquid to evaporate and release these ions into the atmosphere. Further, the ringing of bells and cymbals causes turbulence and these ions are propelled out of the door. All ancient temples have only one door to the sanctum sanctorum, which is surrounded by devotees. These ions energize the devotees and make them feel good.

It is well known in modern science that an excess of negative ions is good for the body and that is why people feel energized when they visit the hills or the sea beaches. When the wind hits hilly surfaces or slopes, or when waves break on the sea beaches, large amounts of negative ions are released. These days, in offices, homes and other closed spaces, modern gadgets called ionizers are used to release negatively charged ions into the environment, to nullify the harmful effects of cigarette smoke and other unhealthy radiations.

Jal Tarpan: In this ancient ritual, devotees face the rising sun with a flat vessel containing water held in front of the body. The vessel is positioned slightly above the chest but below the eyes, and the water is poured to form a column of water, which roughly covers the width of the body and acts as a shield between the sun and the bones of the body. During this ritual, the water column shields the body from the rays of the sun and only allows beneficial ultraviolet rays to penetrate the body.

It is known that ultraviolet rays are very beneficial for the bones in the body but harmful for the eyes. Ultraviolet chambers are now used for therapy during which the patient wears special spectacles to protect the eyes from the ultraviolet rays.

Sprinkling of Water: In ancient times, before any meal, water was sprinkled around the plate or the leaf on which the food was served to form a barrier between the food and the other surroundings. Of course the ground on which people sat or the food was served, was washed and cleaned thoroughly. This was done to ensure that insects on the ground could not cross this water barrier and infect the food. At night, this water served the additional purpose of reflecting natural light to enable people to see what they were eating. With electricity, however, this ritual has become redundant.

Curd and Sugar: In desert areas especially and even in some other areas, local traditions prohibited the eating of certain types of food which induced thirst and would, therefore, need a lot of water for digestion. Even today people eat curd to keep their system cool, and sugar to give them high energy before embarking on a long journey or an important event, such as an examination.

Time Cycles: Day and Night

Not so long ago, in every part of India and even now in most parts of southern India, certain periods of time during the day and night are considered inauspicious to begin a journey, undertake an important task or make critical decisions. However, most modern, educated people consider this to be a superstitious ritual and do not follow it.

During my earlier visits to Chennai, distributors would refuse to come and see me, or if they grudgingly did so, they would not eat or discuss important matters during a period lasting for about one and half hours, which varied every day, and which they referred to as Rahu Kalam.

Scientific observations have found that the earth's magnetic intensities and energy radiations vary during the day. This is perhaps on account of the effect of the sun and the moon on the earth at different times. The chapter 'Subtle Energies of the Human Body' has explained how the body assumes a particular energy dimension during the sun, moon and the earth periods, respectively, which can act separately and concurrently, and which disappears completely at sunset or moon set, or, as in the case of earth energies, at sunrise or moon rise.

In the scriptures, the day from sunrise to sunset has been divided into eight parts, or *kaals*, of one and a half hours each, or in case of a shorter day during the winter, one-eighth of the entire day. At certain time periods during both day and night, the energies of the earth are found to be very low or very high. The low period is known as Rahu Kalam. It was recommended that during this time span, nothing important should be done. The high energy periods are considered auspicious for starting and performing important and exalted functions, like prayer, meditation, study, construction of a house or beginning a journey. One of the highest energy periods occurs uniformly every night between 2 a.m. and 5 a.m.; this is known as the Brahma Muhuratam, meaning, the time allotted by the Creator for creation and realization, which is ideal for activities such as writing, meditation, composing music, and original research. The Rahu Kalam occurs at different times each day of the week. This can be easily remembered by the coined phrase: 'Mother Saw Father Wearing the Turban Sun'. Rahu Kalam occurs from 7.30–9 a.m. on Mondays; 9–10.30 a.m. on Saturdays; 10.30 a.m.–12 noon on Fridays; 12–1.30 p.m. on Wednesdays, and so on, assuming sunrise at 6 a.m. and sunset at 6 p.m. The first time zone or *kaal* after sunrise or sunset is always full of good energy and therefore auspicious (6–7.30 a.m./p.m.). This is the time most appropriate for starting an activity, prayer, planning, and making resolutions.

Touching to Activate

Today there are switches and buttons which need to be put on or pressed to activate any function, whether it is to turn on a fan, an air conditioner, a computer or a nuclear power plant. Similarly it has been an age-old belief that a thought needs to be activated by words and actions. It is important to express love or admiration for someone in words and by deeds rather than just thinking about it.

During prayers in all religions, the centre of the forehead, eyes, ears, nostrils, throat, shoulders, heart, solar plexus and knees are touched to activate them. In a church, the gesture of drawing a cross in front of the body is done with the centre being placed approximately on the solar plexus chakra, the chakra for centring and balancing the body and for enhancing decision making and leadership qualities. The practice of putting a *teeka* (vermillion dot) in the centre of the forehead, which corresponds with the third eye, is a symbolic way of activating the third eye to transmit and receive wisdom.

Positions of Energy for Men and Women

During visits to ancient churches and temples, and having tested people with the Lecher Antenna, I was amazed to find over a period of time, that the energy axis of women was perfectly aligned when they were on the left side of the building, and that of men when they were on the right side. When either gender moved to the other side their energy axis was completely disturbed. Further experiments revealed that these spaces which were known to have distinct characteristics, were specially designed in temples and churches to maximize the energies of men and women, respectively. During weddings and most other religious ceremonies, men are still seated on the right of the women and vice versa. This is an affirmation of this phenomenon.

Clockwise and Anticlockwise Movements

Why does a clock move clockwise? Ever thought of it? Can't it move anticlockwise and show the time equally well? The answer is Yes! It can do so, not only equally well, but better in the southern hemisphere. Why? Because energy moves clockwise in the northern hemisphere, anticlockwise in the southern hemisphere, and straight through at the Equator. In Nairobi, the capital of Kenya, it is often observed by residents and visitors that in some areas, water drains out clockwise and in other colonies, anticlockwise, from a wash basin.

We therefore simulate movements in dance, prayer and everyday work, which follow this principle, so that we are energized. In dance, most rotations in the northern hemisphere, are clockwise. In temples and mosques, we perform a clockwise movement around the deity or sanctum sanctorum.

Often a number of movements generate specific effects. For example, during the sun, moon and earth periods, respectively, certain movements are specified to energize the body. During the sun period we stand facing the east and turn anticlockwise, with a half-circle movement done with eyes open, and the other half with eyes closed. During the moon period, the same movement is started facing east, clockwise. During the earth period we stand facing west and do two sets of movements, clockwise and anticlockwise. It is found that by doing this for two to three minutes during each period everyday, a body is energized greatly.

Washing of Hands and Feet

For ages in India and other parts of the world, before entering a house or a public place, people were encouraged to remove their footwear and wash their hands and feet outside. The purpose was not just to cleanse the exposed parts of the body but also to remove the negative energies, which a person might have absorbed during travel.

In many traditional homes, even today, visitors are requested to remove their footwear outside.

Green Leaves above the Door

A string of green leaves are hung above the door in many houses even now. This was done to dispel any negative energies carried by those entering the door. Leaves do not have to be necessarily used. Anything green can be used as the colour green has cleansing properties. Many people forget to change the green leaves and leave them hanging even after they have become brown and shrivelled. This happens because people put them up blindly, following a ritual without knowing its purpose. Dry and thorny plants and leaves do not emanate positive energies.

Removing Negative Energies from the Body

During my childhood I observed that when any of us was unwell, my grandmother or a maidservant would take a number of spices, including red chillies, in her hand and rotate it around the body from head to toe, a few times, and then burn the mixture on a fire. Often, no smell would emanate. This was surprising as burning chillies normally emanate a strong acrid aroma. Knowing glances would be exchanged and there would be sighs of relief. The operation would be declared successful. This was done when it was suspected that a person, especially a child, had absorbed negative energies and had fallen ill.

The chillies and spices did not emanate a strong smell since the negative energies drawn by them from the ill person's body destroyed their aroma and fragrance.

Naming Ceremony/Baptism

In every civilization, a child is named normally after he begins to speak. This is a major ceremony, which incorporates chants, affirmations and other rituals. Names given in most ancient civilizations embodied the qualities and achievements parents desired for their child. Often, the name of a famous personality who has achieved great success or elicited reverence and devotion from people, is given to the child. Baptism in Christianity or the Janaeu ceremony in Hinduism is performed to induct a child into the faith or a way of life. The child is made to take certain vows and make affirmations, either himself or through his elders, which will help him lead a life of virtue and purpose. A learned and celibate person normally performs the ritual. A special feature of this process is touching various parts of the body, as elaborated earlier, with chants, to energize, activate and empower them.

Discovery through Observation

Most rituals evolved from prolonged observation and a sensitive attempt to understand various phenomena that affected human lives. A similar process also led to important scientific discoveries. Most inventors repeated an experiment or observed a happening hundreds of times before claiming that they had discovered something. Our ancients used observations to enhance their day-to-day lives often without documenting the reasons for the same.

Observations have helped people predict weather patterns, pre-empt calamities and health disorders. For instance, the whining of a dog was understood to be a precursor to a storm or an earthquake or a man-made calamity.

The highly developed intuitive abilities of animals enable them to sense disorders under the earth's surface and seismic shifts, as well as the changes in temperature of the air and its cyclic movement, that could cause an earthquake or a storm. Before the Tsunami tragedy, elephants in the Andaman Islands had broken their shackles and retreated deep into the forest. Other animals also did so. They could all sense the seismic shift and vibrations well before it happened. Tribals, who have not been exposed to civilization and rely on nature for both their subsistence and pleasure, develop great sensitivity and communion with nature. Tribals in the Andamans were also able to save their own lives because they were able to apprehend the calamity well in advance.

Animals can also sense from miles away the vibes emanating from people advancing with negative or aggressive intent. A pet does not lick his master the same way as he used to earlier if his master has developed an affliction like cancer. The pet often comes near, sniffs, makes a whining sound and goes away, even before a person is indisposed.

Cows, dogs and horses are known to seek and thrive in positive environments and so consciously seek positively charged spaces. That was one reason why they were domesticated. Cows in India are worshipped as pure and also because their dung enriches the soil and their milk provides nourishment.

People living in rural, agrarian societies are trained from childhood to predict the weather by observing the sky, the sun and the moon. This enables them to decide when to travel, and when to plant seeds and harvest crops. Once while I was driving through Europe with an Austrian friend, he showed me some thin streaks in the sunny sky and predicted heavy rain within two hours. Sure enough, the bright sunshine soon dissolved into a downpour! Subsequently, I have often observed this phenomenon and have found that rain would follow within two to twelve hours of the prediction. During a visit with friends to Ramgarh, in Uttaranchal, I showed them some streaks just before sunset and predicted that there would be a heavy downpour before sunrise. They jeered in disbelief and to rub it in further, confirmed from a group of village elders that my prediction was preposterous and no rain was likely at least for the next four days. Around 5.30

in the morning the downpour began.

Similarly, a haze or a diffused halo around the moon at night is a certain precursor to rain within 12–24 hours.

Six months before the rainy season people in villages used to observe when and in what part of a tree the birds made their nests. If they nested later it would indicate that the rains would be delayed. If the nests were made in the lowest part of the tree, a drought was imminent; if it was made in the middle, normal rainfall could be expected, and if in the highest part of the tree, excessive rainfall and floods were certain.

In the hills, on the oak and deodar trees, vegetation and leaves grow on their bark because of moss. Once they start disappearing, one can be certain that the monsoon is over.

Conclusion

It is important that in this era of knowledge, rituals are analyzed and understood. If they are still relevant, they should continue to be practised. If not, they should be modified or discarded, and new rituals which can be understood and practised easily by people, should be created. Observation should be used, as was done earlier, to discover or rediscover unexplained phenomena to enhance the quality of our lives and the well-being of our environment, our planet and the universe—for this indeed is the purpose of rituals.

8

The Earth—Our Mother

She holds us
To her bosom
With gravity.
She gives us
Mountains to climb
Rivers to swim in
Food to nourish us
Water to quench our thirst.
From and on Her
Dwellings emerge
To protect us from
The heat of the sun
The chill of rain and
The fury of the wind.
From Her, Upon Her
We embark on a journey
Beyond a beginning,
Without an end.

In chapter 3, 'The Eternal Elements', we discussed the earth as an element. It goes without saying that the earth is the planet on which we live, which makes possible our existence every moment. It sustains and nourishes us. It is part of a galaxy of our universe, which also includes the sun and the moon and many other planets.

The earth orbits around the sun at a speed of about 0.1 million km per hour and takes one year to complete one orbit. It covers a distance of 958 million km. However we feel as if the earth is stationary.

The moon along with the earth also travels round the sun, at the same speed as the earth, though its rotation around the earth is quite distinct.

If we divide the distance of the sun from the earth by the diameter of the sun, or if we divide the distance of the moon by the diameter of the moon, we get the figure 108. This is considered to be the magic figure, which is also derived by multiplying the number of planets (nine) by the number of constellations (twelve). This figure is considered to be sacred in the Indian subcontinent. A prayer is chanted 108 times and a rosary has 108 beads.

The earth is the only physical object which is known to rotate on three axes. It rotates on its own axis, which is inclined at 22 degrees. It rotates around the sun, and the entire galaxy consisting of the sun, moon and the earth together rotate around other galaxies in the universe.

Sitting, standing or travelling on the earth, we are rotating, spinning and travelling at phenomenal speeds along with the earth though we do not feel the effects at all. How does this happen? Obviously there are forces holding us or grounding us, so that we do not experience this movement. This is the gravitational pull of the earth.

This comes from the core of the earth, which comprises highly magnetic molten or volcanic substances. The magnetic forces are effective only up to a distance of approximately 10 km all around the earth known as the stratosphere. The heat and other gases emanating from the earth combine with ions and form an envelope around the earth, which is held to the earth by its magnetic force.

Without a stratosphere, we would not be able to breathe and would not be held to the earth if the gravitational forces did not hold us; instead we would be flung away and would go spinning somewhere far away into the universe. When we are travelling on a plane, which is flying at a height of almost 10 km above the earth's surface, we are travelling at a relative speed of say 1000 km per hour, which is in addition to the 1670 km per hour speed at which the earth rotates around its own axis.

This phenomena lends itself to language usage. We often refer to a person being 'brought down to earth' or to reality. A 'down-to-earth' person is one we can trust and rely upon.

Intensity of Magnetic Forces

Are these magnetic pulls or the intensity of the magnetic forces constant? As we climb the stratosphere, they obviously reduce. In fact, it has been noticed that beyond 100 feet above the earth's surface, the force reduces by more than 15 per cent—enough to make people feel disoriented and not sufficiently rooted to the ground. During earthquakes, it is found that damage to buildings, which are more than seven storeys, is much greater. In fact, buildings more than six levels high are designed with special earthquake resistant materials and features.

Do the other planets, particularly the sun and moon, influence the magnetic and gravitational forces of the earth? It has been conclusively found that the intensity of the magnetic forces does not remain constant throughout but varies during different times of the day and night. Later in this chapter we will discuss in further detail how in ancient India this concept was well researched, documented and used in day-to-day life.

Geo-biology

Geo means earth, bio—energy, and logy—science. Geo-biology, also known as geomancy in the US, is a science which deals with the study of various types of the earth's energies as well as methods to detect, measure, understand and deal with them.

Research has shown that the earth's magnetic field is not a blanket but a maze of grids of energy lines, which emanate from the surface of the earth and circumscribe the globe.

Dr Ernst Hartman, a German physician, discovered these grid lines, which is why they are known as the Hartman Grid. According to him they are complex but have definite patterns.

These lines are oriented in a north-south and east-west direction at 4-10 m intervals. The resulting energy field is called telluric (earth) energy.

Dr Currie, a French scientist, later established the existence of the diagonal grids, which run from north-east to south-west and from south-east to north-west, or north-west to south-east and south-west to north-east. These are called cosmic energy grids, because they are not formed solely by the earth's forces but by non-gravitational and other planetary influences.

In combination both these grid formations are known as cosmo-telluric energy grids. These energies too, like the energies of the subtle body, and like electricity, are bio-electromagnetic in nature.

The alignment of buildings, materials, and even the human body with respect to these energies has a distinct effect on our well-being.

Magnetic Grid Lines

That the existence of these energy grid lines was known to the people in ancient times is proven by the way structures were made in different civilizations and parts of the world which apparently had no communication with one another. The old monasteries in the Himalayan region placed the structures and cells for monks in such a way that they were contained within the grid lines, in what normally is a neutral zone. The Romans oriented all the buildings in their villages, towns and cities with respect to the cardinal BEM grids. All their roads of conquest followed large BEM grids, with energy lines called Maximus Maximorum, at a spacing of 2-3 km. They manipulated these grids to render them positive, thereby reducing fatigue amongst their marching soldiers.

In ancient India the cardinal and diagonal grids were used in the concept of eight *dishas* or orientations, especially in the alignment of temples and other structures. The importance given to orientation in Vaastu Shastra is based on the deeper understanding of the alignment of the subtle energies of the human body, which are affected by the orientations of the building with respect to electromagnetic gridlines.

While planning large human settlements and townships, ancients in Europe used a simple yet very effective method to map the grid lines along the earth's surface. They let goats or sheep graze freely in that area. The herds would not eat the grass along the lines because they could sense the negative radiations being emitted. The zones where the grass had been eaten were used for living and working spaces, and the internal and external walls were built above the grid lines.

By using cows, a similar process was used for locating and building temples. Cats are found to thrive on negative energy and always sit on or near BEM grid nodes to recharge themselves. This may be the reason why cats are always shown as companions of witches. Ants are also known to locate their anthills on similar negative grid nodes and so do the bees for their beehives. These points are harmful for a human being. On the other hand, horses, cows, sheep and dogs always find positive or neutral energy ground to recharge themselves.

Man has not completely lost his instincts with respect to these invisible energies. Children, and sometimes adults too, restlessly move around in sleep till their bodies locate the least disturbing zone and orient themselves accordingly.

The obvious question that arises is, if walls were built on the grid lines, were they not susceptible to being damaged by negative radiations? The answer is Yes, they normally should have! However, they were not. This was so because in older buildings hollow walls were constructed in order to provide better insulation against heat, cold and sound. It was found that the walls were so positioned that the grid lines went through their hollow portions.

The cutting or intersection of grid lines in modern buildings can be easily identified even by the uninitiated. We can see these grid lines on boundary walls and other walls as vertical cracks which run zigzag from top to bottom and are repeated at almost equal distances. This is also seen in fairly new buildings. As the buildings become older the cracks tend to become more pronounced.

While people living on higher floors of high rises, say on the fifteenth or twentieth floor, experience a feeling of not being grounded or rootless, the good news for them is that the effect of the negative grid lines also becomes weaker and causes less harm to them as compared to those living on the fifth or eighth floor.

We will discuss methods of correction in a subsequent chapter. After correcting the negative effect of the grid lines, it was found that cracks in some existing buildings disappeared or became less visible within one year.

Types of Magnetic Grids

BEM grids are of four types: major, principal, normal and subsidiary.

While major, principal and normal grid lines are perpendicular to the earth's surface, the subsidiary grid lines emanate at an angle varying between 30-45 degrees from the earth's surface, depending upon the topography and the nature of the surface.

The major grids are 15-17 m wide and are sometimes placed a few kilometres apart from one another. The principal

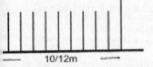

.1 Principal BEM Radiations
(Ten sub-lines)

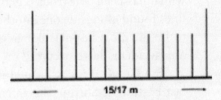

Fig. 8.2 Major BEM Radiations
(Twelve sub-lines)

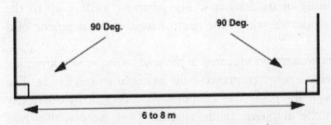

Fig. 8.3 Normal Lines of Earth Radiations
(No sub-lines within)

grids are 10-12 m wide. The normal grids are 6-8 m wide. It is customary to find two normal grids back to back or a normal grid separating two principal grids. A major grid has twelve sub-lines, a principal—ten, and the normal grid has no sub-lines.

What does all this mean and how do we use this knowledge?

The major grids are used for larger public or utility spaces, not separated by walls. The principal grids are used for smaller spaces or houses. The normal grids are used most commonly for pathways to churches, temples, roads and busy thoroughfares, where a large number of people or vehicles ply. Since these grids do not have any subsidiary lines, the people using these spaces are therefore not subjected to negative radiations. The Champs Élysée, the main boulevard in Paris, is a prime example of a very busy thoroughfare, which has been constructed between two sets of normal grid lines found alongside one another, back to back. It continues to be the most popular congregation place in Paris. Hardly any accidents have occurred on this busy boulevard.

The Gingee Fort is located near Pondicherry. It was the last bastion of Shivaji, the valiant Maratha king who was a thorn in the flesh of the Mughals for many years. He not only outwitted them with cleverness but with bravery too. The design features of the Gingee Fort offer glimpses of the ingenuity of its designers. The pathway leading up to the fort is located within the neutral zone of the magnetic grid lines.

Its granary was located in the south-east, which provided the vital energy to preserve the material stored inside. The roofs of the protective canopies were designed to perfectly align the magnetic fields around. They were within two intersecting grids and their heights corresponded with the

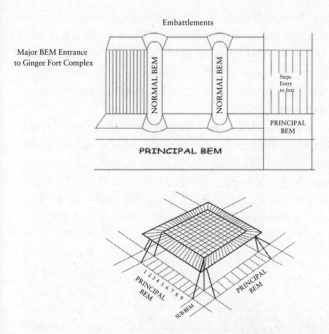

Fig. 8.4 The Gingee Fort

height at which the inclined radiations from a nearby grid reached their roof. This made the structure stronger as the magnetic forces flowed along and not through or across the structure. This Fort, though abandoned many years ago, still seems to be naturally well preserved, perhaps because it is designed in perfect harmony with the Earth's forces.

The **Temple of Mahabalipuram,** in Tamil Nadu, a state in southern India, was taken up as a research project by the Sri Aurobindo Ashram to study the arrangement of magnetic grid lines in the temple complex and the placement of structures with respect to these lines. The effects of temple energies on the human body were also studied. It was found that the pathways leading to the temple were located within neutral grid lines so that the people walking on these pathways were not subjected to any radiations. The temple itself was placed between two major grids and the twenty-four subdivisions of these grids coincided exactly with small minarets, which had the effect of converting their energy flows from negative to positive.

It was also found that as a person ascended the steps to the temple, the energy axis of his leg zone, which was disturbed earlier, got aligned. When he reached just outside the sanctum sanctorum the body energies were aligned, and within it the head energies were aligned. This temple still has such a powerful effect on people even though no worship has taken place in the temple for hundreds of years.

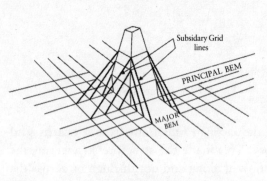

Even in the Bahai temple, in New Delhi, the pathways are within neutral grid lines.

In the case of the Acropolis, in Athens, the temple is located between a major axis.

Fig. 8.5 Grid Lines of a Builiding

As shown in Fig. 8.4 on the Gingee Fort the canopy subdivisions were met by the radiations from the subsidiary grid whose sub lines, unlike other types of grids, are inclined. In the case of subsidiary grids it is found that half the lines are inclined upwards on one side and the other half on the other side. This phenomenon was often used to accurately plan the floor heights of residential and other structures in case of a tall building (see Fig. 8.5).

It is well known and can be seen today too, that most old buildings have unequal floor heights which increase with succeeding levels to correspond exactly with the place where the subsidiary lines meet these buildings. This also takes care of the perspective effect whereby the human eye perceives the higher floors to be smaller if they are equal in height to the lower floors. The floors of the older buildings, when perceived with the naked eye, seem equal.

Neutralizing Effects

Are there ways to neutralize the effects of magnetic grids over large distances?

The answer to this is also Yes! Our ancients used rock-like structures called menhirs and dolmens, on the nodes of magnetic grids. These acted as transmitters and receivers of energy. The menhirs located on the nodes reversed the nature of the flow turning it into a positive radiation and transmitted it to a radius of almost 18 km. Many dolmens that were lower and flatter structures, were located between the menhirs to receive these energies and spread them along the earth's surface.

Last year, during my visit to Stonehenge, UK, with a colleague, we found that the tall monoliths (some partly and others severely damaged) arranged in a circular formation, covered two major BEM grids along the north-south and east-west direction. Each stone was on one of the twelve subsidiary lines. The effect is so powerful that it neutralizes the negative effects of the grid lines up to a distance of 2 km all around. The thousands of people who visit this historical site sit or stand mesmerized for hours, apparently for no rhyme or reason. When queried, they admit that they are not able to comprehend why they stayed there so long. We were, like many others, awed and energized.

The Ajanta caves in India, which house some of the most amazing three-dimensional and well-proportioned paintings and sculptures ever created as far back as the first century BC, give us an amazing insight into the advanced architectural styles and clothing that existed at that time, and which were exported to Rome and other parts of Europe. These twenty-six caves are arranged in a horse-shoe arrangement on the hillsides surrounding the river Baghola. Each cave has a statue of Lord Buddha or a stupa, which is a symbolic representation of Buddha. We found that the magnetic grid lines were completely neutralized in the whole area and the energy level, even after years of neglect and decay, was between 100 thousand to 200 thousand million Bovis, which is perhaps the highest recorded.

People have found simple ways to generate the same effect by using flat copper pieces with clockwise spirals inscribed on them. These act as a combination of the dolmen and the menhir, when fixed or positioned accurately on the nodes of intersecting grid lines. They reverse the movement or the flow of the radiation from anticlockwise to clockwise and spread it along the adjoining grid lines. Their effects can last for a few metres, approximately 10-30 metres, depending on the type of land and structure. The spirals can also be put at two ends of a particular grid line within a space. In the southern hemisphere, anticlockwise spirals are used.

Variations in the Intensity of the Earth's Radiations

Our research has revealed that the intensity of the earth's grid lines is not consistent during both the day and the night, but follows cyclic variations, which correspond exactly with the Indian concept of *kaal* and *ghadi* (time periods). The periods from sunrise to sunset and sunset to sunrise are each divided into eight *ghadis* of equal duration. Even to this day the calendars of the year are marked with these *ghadis*. Some of the *ghadis* like Rahu Kalam and Yamagam are considered inauspicious since they correspond to negative and low intensity periods. While the reason for the variations is still a subject of research, it is amazing how our forefathers had an exact and intimate knowledge of even these details which they dealt with to minimize ill effects. During my visits to Chennai and other parts of south India, our distributors and clients refused to meet or sign important documents and conduct business during these periods. The timings of the *kaals* during the days of the week can be conveniently remembered by the phrase mentioned earlier, 'Mother Saw Father Wearing The Turban Son' – Monday, Saturday, Friday, Wednesday, Thursday, Tuesday, Sunday. The first one and half hour *kaal* after sunrise occurs on Monday, the second *kaal* between one and a half and three hours after sunrise on Saturday, the third on Friday, then on Wednesday, Thursday, Tuesday and the last, just before sunset, on Sunday.

Underground Water Streams and Cavities

If there is a cavity under the earth through which air or water flows, the flow of the earth's energy is obstructed. The energy flow upwards from the sides of the cavity, moves anticlockwise with great force and emanates from the surface of the earth. A line of maximum intensity, which is negative, is formed all along the length of this cavity at the centre. Its effect too can be neutralized, by reversing the flow with the copper spiral located end to end on the line of maximum intensity, which can be located with scientific instruments.

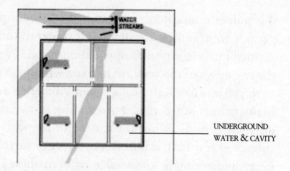

Fig. 8.6 Impact of Underground Water

Let us look at Fig. 8.6. The bed in the bedroom in the top left hand corner is partly placed over an underground water stream. This bed would need to be shifted to the opposite or the adjacent walls. The choice of wall against which the bed is placed would depend on orientation. We have earlier discussed that while sleeping, the head should be in the south or east.

How does the underground water stream affect people or spaces? The part of the body of the person on the bed, which is bisected by the underground water stream is most likely to get affected. The effects on various people would vary depending upon their immunity level and the genetic strength of their body. The condition would be aggravated with the passage of time. It has also been found that these parts of the body develop water retention or air retention diseases, like hydrocele and tuberculosis, or pneumonia, depending on whether the cavity contains water or air.

The Cathedral of Chartres in France has a complex design of columns and arches, which are built on underground water streams below the floor. They are designed in a manner which makes them draw in the energy emanating from the water streams and reverse their flow clockwise, just like the menhirs and dolmens do in the case of magnetic grid lines. This energy is then spread throughout the church.

Similar design principals have been used in the church at Cologne in Germany, and the chapel at the Duomo in Milan.

The Lecher Antenna

The Lecher Antenna works on the same principal as the water divining or other dowsing instruments or materials. Its design and versatility is the result of the ingenuity of Dr Ernst Lecher, an Austrian physicist, who invented it.

Dr Ersnt Lecher was a house physician who during his practice of twenty years, while visiting the same houses, found that though different families inhabited a particular house at different times, they all contracted the same kind of diseases. This led him to research the kind of radiations present in a house. For example, he discovered that people subjected to large electrical radiations from transmission lines running parallel to the house were prone to cancer; those sleeping under low ceilings, blood pressure; underground water streams, water retention; and on magnetic grid lines (which had been discovered by then), general weakening of the part of the body being cut by the grid lines.

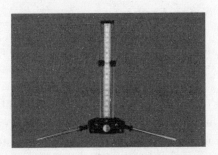

Fig. 8.7 The Lecher Antenna

The challenge was to design an instrument, which was simple to carry and use without sacrificing accuracy. The instrument needed to cover a spectrum of radiations and wavelengths to which people were likely to be subjected. He found that all wavelengths less than 20 cm which was the wavelength of the cell of the human body, affected the body and those above 20 cm had no effect on the body.

The Lecher Antenna is an antenna bent on itself, that is, there are two arms at 90 degrees to the vertical arm. The vertical portion is a calibrated scale of 20 cm with a moving cursor. It also has two inclined horizontal rods joined to the scale. The cursor is fixed at a particular wavelength, depending upon the type of radiation to be measured. When this is done, a standing wave is formed. The antenna is held at a particular tension by the scanner and a person or a space is scanned. The antenna resonates and moves when it encounters a similar wavelength in the body or atmosphere.

While the results and accuracy of the findings do depend on the skill and sensitivity of the person using the antenna, the modern variation of the instrument is fairly easy to learn and use. It is much more precise than any other dowsing instrument developed so far, especially for outdoor use.

Materials of the Earth

The earth comprises mud, sand, rocks, stones, minerals, liquids of various viscosities, metals and crystals. They have formations underground, which support life and intricate formations of icicles. Each mineral and metal has distinct properties of conduction, radiation, wavelengths and porosity. They are found in layers, sometimes running for miles and with thickness varying from a few centimetres to even a mile.

Their formation takes centuries and involves varying degrees of compression and myriad types of chemical reactions. Crystals are beings of light, which are trapped for years under the earth's surface. Their interaction with minerals and rocks imparts colour and certain properties, which can be either beneficial or harmful, when used by people in houses or as ornaments. Crystals, especially cut and polished ones, can absorb and reflect light and energy. They can have powerful effects and should not be strewn around only for decorative effect. They need to be correctly placed in spaces which have natural sunlight and need to be cleaned often with salt water or by keeping them exposed to the sun for 10 to 15 minutes.

The earth creates, supports and nurtures the life of men, materials and structures. They are made by its constituents, supported by it and when the time is ripe, submerged by it and consecrated inside. All people and animals are similarly consecrated, to eventually disintegrate or turn into ash.

9

The Sanctity of Spaces

In heart and mind
Beneath the sky,
on the earth
Are Spaces—
Monuments and homes
Imagination and reality
Wedded by dreams
Which inhabit our consciousness
And ignite creativity.

When we look at the open sky or the horizon, space seems to be undefined and endless. It is only defined by the power and limit of our vision. When we are within a closed space surrounded by walls, we know that there are vistas beyond. A person living in a house or working in an office without windows is invariably pale, irritable and unhappy. The physical and mental condition of people in solitary confinement is well known and documented.

So what is special about spaces—finite and infinite, big and small? What is their significance? Can they make a difference and bring positive changes into our lives?

The answer to all these questions is in the affirmative.

Spaces can make us happy or sad and change our lives in a myriad ways.

In the following pages, I will try and share with you some ways to understand, select, define, correct and use spaces to enhance well-being and efficiency.

Space: Reality or Imagination

Don't we often say we create our own space. Be it a dwelling space, our workplace, a garden or recreation areas, we have the power to choose where we wish to be.

The most sacred and beautiful monuments, cities and landscapes owe their origin to imagination or a vision which flashed just once as a revelation or repeatedly, either in dreams or when awake.

Space is not limited to what we see and create but extends to what we can imagine.

Many people have aspired to convert their dreams into reality, by drawing and building, or just by sharing their vision and ideas with others who have made the creation of an object, a temple, a statue or a space their own mission.

A space or contour then is a position we are at currently, or a projection of our memory into the future or the past to make it our present.

Landscapes

When we conceive of a landscape we probably think of open spaces, greenery, flat or undulating land, a stream meandering past, flowers, trees, hills, valleys, beautiful houses. More often than not, however, such mental images evoke mere wistfulness. Certainly none of us would like our home to be on the edge of a cliff or just below a high mountain. None of us would like to see a bare high wall just a few feet in front of our door or window, or be surrounded by taller buildings than our own. None of us would like to feel hemmed in.

But how many of us can change our surroundings in today's world crammed with concrete and mortar! We certainly cannot wave a magic wand and turn walls into valleys! What we can do though is create what is required or eliminate the undesirable to counter the ill effects of negative energies around us. And how would we do that? By building a wall or a hedge on the edge of the cliff in front of our house, closing the window on the side of the mountain or plant trees and flowers on it, growing trees and creepers between our house and taller buildings around, or painting the bare wall in front of our door and window with a beautiful landscape.

When people needed protection from the wind and attacks from invaders, they built their houses in valleys. Those who did not particularly crave the company of others built a home on top of a hill. Feng Shui, the Chinese science of energizing space, suggests that a hill behind the house supports the people who live there. Those who do not have access to such a feature are advised to put a picture of a hilly landscape at the rear portion of the house. Vaastu Shastra, the Indian science of architecture, recommends an entrance in the north or the east, which should also be lower than the south or the west in order to receive the beneficial energies of the earth and the cosmos. The rear part of the house should be in the south or west and higher than the front, which would be in the north-east or north-west.

This does not mean or imply that people who have entrances in the south or west or those whose plots are higher in the north or west are doomed. Nature and ingenuity can always create alternatives. In Indian homes, a Swastika on the sides of the door, equidistant from top to bottom, and a picture of Lord Ganesha on top of the door, are often used. These symbols succeed in correcting the energy flows into the building even if the doors are incorrectly positioned.

Homes

Homes should be clean, comfortable, healthy and inspiring. Seems like a tall order? Not really. We can keep our homes clean by removing our footwear outside so that we do not carry dirt inside, not cooking foul-smelling food, arranging our belongings tidily and not creating clutter.

We can create a feeling of space by using minimal furniture, appliances and artefacts. Our houses are meant to be homes, not warehouses or museums. Homes that allow adequate cross-ventilation and sunshine are healthy to live in. Obviously, one of the ways that this can be done is by ensuring that the doors and windows are correctly placed.

Vaastu Shastra is a treatise on how to build and use spaces, to maximize the beneficial effects of the environment. It owes its origin to the ancient texts—the Vedas and the Shastras. It is a very powerful and effective science, the correct application of which helps us achieve harmony and balance, without sacrificing prosperity and spiritual aspirations. However, since this science was passed on orally, some distortions have occurred over the years. In addition, many of the present practitioners do not fully understand the rationale behind a particular theory or prescription. They try to apply ancient norms to modern homes and offices, completely disregarding the fact that the context, traditions as well as living and work styles have altered drastically from what was prevalent 3000 years ago. The science has to be suitably adapted and developed to serve present-day needs and realities.

Other effective knowledge systems and methodologies were developed and used effectively in almost all ancient civilizations, especially in China, Latin America and Rome. They are founded on similar principles, but the practice varies according to the topography, prevalent local traditions and living habits.

The reason Feng-Shui is very popular all over the world is that it is strong on interpretation and uses a lot of symbolic interventions to correct negative influences and create a sense of well-being. For instance, coins are kept in certain spaces within the house to depict and attract wealth. Pictures denoting happiness and other symbols like statues of the laughing Buddha to generate well-being, and photographs or statues of learned people to inspire wisdom are used. Chimes and water fountains are used to circulate Chi or energy, and also to create sounds that generate good vibrations.

Vaastu is less popular worldwide and more restricted within the Indian diaspora because its practitioners have chosen largely to keep the knowledge to themselves and not explain it to lay persons in simple ways. They also prescribe solutions, which are difficult to implement and tend to have a rigid and inflexible approach.

We at Syenergy, with our research and subsequent understanding and the use of modern instruments, have found ways to detect, measure and validate various phenomena. Simple, non-destructive and effective solutions have been discovered and used extensively to correct energy flows within a space, to enhance health, improve interpersonal relationships and efficiency. This has been done by using small coloured dots, flat copper pieces with symbols of the spiral, other symbols like the Swastika, Om, and pictures of deities or stones placed strategically in various directions.

Spaces: Good and Bad

All of us have, at times, experienced feelings of discomfort even in the most opulent and well-decorated houses. On the other hand, we have often felt very relaxed in surroundings, which may be sparse and small. This is mainly due to the subtle electromagnetic radiations or energies within those spaces, which affect us in very definite and tangible ways.

Can we measure their effects? Yes, we can.

How? By recording the pulse rate or blood pressure of a person using that space, both inside the space and outside. A lower count generally denotes a higher degree of body comfort. The same method can be used before and after correcting a space to ascertain the efficacy of the corrections. Electroencephalograms (EEGs) can also be recorded before and after the non-destructive corrections have been made.

How do these energies emanate? Where do they come from? What causes them to flow in a certain manner? What is the difference between positive and negative energies? These and many other questions need to be answered.

Energies and their flows are governed by phenomena like the shape of the plot and the structure; relative slopes of the land, floor and roof of the structure; types of materials used in construction; location and size of doors and windows, and various other aspects.

The placing of the structure in a plot requires careful planning. The building should be located in the most desirable part, or quadrant, of the plot, followed by other quadrants, which are less preferable, and then those where it is least desirable to locate a building. Similarly, within the building it is important to locate members of the family in specific areas, and to allocate preferred spaces for certain functions. For example, the kitchen should preferably be located in the south-east or north-west, and the master bedroom in the south-west or north-east. Placing a factory, boilers, generators, and electrical items in the south-east or north-west, and the office of the CEO, the Accounts/Administration department in the south-west or north-east are advisable. Furthermore, the placement of objects, furniture, cooking and electrical appliances, electrical points, drainage pipes and other objects create their own energy flows, which could have a negative impact on certain spaces, and consequently on the people inhabiting those spaces. Vaastu propounds that drains drain away energy from the built space and should not be located within. Checking energy flows with the Lecher Antenna or the pendulum does confirm that energies near and around drains become negative. Similarly, it has been found that electrical points and sources of electrical current like TVs and microwaves have harmful effects which can be rectified by using colours and copper symbols as described in earlier chapters.

Positive or Negative Energies

What is the nature of these energies? Can they be quantified and measured? Do they emanate from the realm of imagination or do they have a scientific basis?

These energies, like electricity, are bio-electromagnetic in nature. They can be detected and measured with scientific instruments. Their flow can be altered and enhanced by symbols, mirrors and colours in the same manner as a microchip would absorb, transmit or alter radiations and data. We have all experienced static charge from clothes, paper and objects that are quite different from electricity and are in fact, a manifestation of these subtle BEM energies.

In addition to energies induced by the shape, size,

Fig. 9.1 Fibonacci Numbers   Fig. 9.2 Golden Ratio

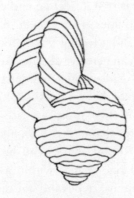

Fig. 9.3 Spiral Shape

construction and location of a built space, strong energies emanate from magnetic grid lines (as described in the chapter 'The Earth—Our Mother'), and the cavities of the earth formed by underground water streams and clefts or fissures caused by volcanic eruptions. Radiations also emanate from electrical current and appliances. Stones used for construction or for decoration also have different radiations, as do colours and plants. The understanding of how to use these in certain spaces can deplete or enhance the energies within a space and change the nature of energy flows from negative to positive.

VAASTU SHASTRA AND OTHER ANCIENT PRACTICES

Shape of the Plot and Building

The most preferred plot shapes are squares, circles or rectangles. For work and dwelling units, square and rectangular shapes are preferred, since it is easy to define and construct definite spaces for specific activities within them. A square leads to efficient use of space and a feeling of comfort, since a person standing in the centre can perceive all sides equally well. It also enables good circulation of energies and functional movement. A rectangle with a ratio of the two sides as 1:1.614 is considered the most beneficial for circulation of energies as it perfectly houses the classic spiral shape (Fig. 9.3), a simulator of high and infinite energy. Round shapes can be used for public monuments and to define shapes within as well as outside buildings, namely, columns, arches and staircases. For overhead beams, and in the case of columns and staircases where design or functional requirements do not allow a round shape, it is beneficial to round off the edges.

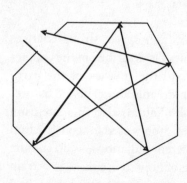

Fig. 9.4 Many-sided plots

Plots that have irregular shapes or are many sided are best avoided. In the case of the former, space usage becomes inefficient. In addition, one quadrant—either north-west, north-east, south-west or south-east is reduced in size and importance. The use of multisided plots creates jagged energy flows and agitation (see Fig. 9.4). You can imagine a ball bouncing in the space to imagine the

agitation that can be created. The only exception is the case
when the shape is elongated in the north-east. This is so,
because the energies of the earth flow from the north-east.

The slope within the plot and the building and the relative
heights of the different parts of the building are also governed
by these energy flows. The north and the east should be lower,
and the south and west, higher.

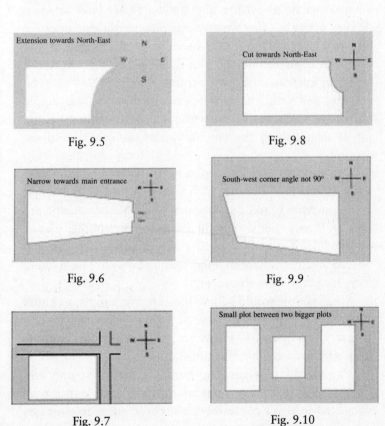

Extension towards North-East

Fig. 9.5

Narrow towards main entrance

Fig. 9.6

Fig. 9.7

Figs. 9.5, 9.6, 9.7
Desirable Plot Shapes

Cut towards North-East

Fig. 9.8

South-west corner angle not 90°

Fig. 9.9

Small plot between two bigger plots

Fig. 9.10

Figs. 9.8, 9.9, 9.10
Undesirable Plot Shapes

Vaastu practitioners talk about the *dosha* or fault in a plot. Prayers are performed and offerings made to neutralize these effects and change the energy flows.

Surrounding Areas

While we can take care of matters within our plot or structure, what do we do about the surrounding areas? How severely do they affect us? Can we do something to mitigate negative effects of say, a mountain in front of the house in the north, or a pit behind the plot in the south, or a very tall building surrounding our habitat. Their effects may be negative and would have to be examined on site and simple corrective measures taken without actually filling up the pit or demolishing the mountain and the other buildings around.

The areas around a plot or a house have to be examined to check whether there are high tension lines near them, and if certain types of trees, graveyards or a place of worship are nearby. If so, either we should decide to take another plot or a house, or carry out energetic corrections to isolate their ill effects/negative radiations. High tension lines have been found to reduce immunity to cancer.

Many people would believe that a public temple, a church or a mosque adjoining a house or within the boundaries of a house is auspicious. However, this is not so. Sounds preposterous, even blasphemous, doesn't it?

The energies of such monuments are so strong and overpowering that a normal human body cannot be subjected to them constantly. Moreover, these monuments are visited by a constant stream of devotees who cause tremendous energy turbulence around the house. These energies are largely negative. Such structures should be at least ten to fifteen metres away. If this is not possible, some virtual barriers have to be created.

Effect of Materials

The excessive presence of materials like quartzite and granite in a plot can create negative energies and need to be either removed from the site of construction or their effect has to be neutralized by other means. An effective way is to use lime powder to layer the entire foundation or base of the structure to neutralize the effect of negative radiations and create good conductivity for the earth's energies.

Within buildings the use of natural materials like rubber for insulation, vegetable paints for painting, lime mortar for brickwork and marble or various types or lime stones for flooring and cladding is considered most desirable. Excessive use of synthetic material or derived products creates energy blockage and retards natural flows of energies within the structure and generates static charge.

It has been found in the study of older buildings in Europe that the usage of natural building material was almost 70 per cent and the balance was vegetable material, whereas in recently built houses, the use of hard and synthetic material has shot up to 60-70 per cent. Synthetic materials obstruct the natural flow of energies in spaces like they do on bodies.

Use of reinforced concrete in floors, beams, columns and slabs causes a cage-like effect, which is also known as the Faraday Effect. This phenomenon is caused by an excessive number of positive ions being released in the atmosphere since the negative ions are drawn in by the steel reinforcement. As we know, an excess of negative ions in the atmosphere is beneficial for the body. This effect can be countered to a large extent by using lime mortar in the foundations and walls.

It is also important while using materials like wood, lime, stone slabs and marble to study the grain structure of the same and try to place it in the same orientation as its place of origin. The craftsmen who used these materials in earlier times did ensure that this orientation was respected. Imagine your door to be a tree and the tree to be placed upside down. Improper placement causes reversal in energy flow, which causes discomfort and ill health. In ancient forts, the steps were constructed with the negatively charged surface of the stone facing outwards. The steps were also high and narrow. The idea was to make it difficult for an invading army to climb up quickly and subject it constantly to negative radiation. This made it easier for the defending army to fight the invaders.

Granite and mirrors should be used only on the external façade of the building, if at all, and not within work chambers, bedrooms and other living and working areas. Mirrors bounce back energies and should not be placed in front of the bed since sleeping areas require calm and tranquil energies. They should also not be placed facing the entrance or the workplace as they would bounce back the energies trying to enter inside.

It is often seen that children and sensitive adults avoid sleeping in that part of the bed cut by a mirror. When a mirror is in the centre of the bed shared by a married couple, they find themselves away from each other on either edge of the bed in the morning though they may have slept close to one another in the centre at night.

It is often beyond our control and means to follow some or all the things that are prescribed. To begin with, we seldom build our own houses or flats. However, the remedies and corrections are given and illustrated at the end of the chapter.

Position of the Building within the Plot

To allow maximum energies to flow into the plot, it is recommended that if the plot is much larger than the structure proposed to be built on it, the maximum and highest built area should be in the south-west, followed by the south-east and then, the north-west. The north-east should be vacant and clean. However, if the building is likely to occupy all quadrants, the north-east should be the lowest in height. If this is not possible, put an angle or a rod of a suitable length at the edge of the quadrant or corner that you wish to raise so that it becomes the highest point in the building.

It is obvious that more land should be vacant in the north and east as compared to the south or west to allow energies to flow in from the north and the east and settle in the south and the west.

Location of Doors

Doors allow energies to enter and flow into a house. Naturally, they should open inwards to allow that to happen. Moreover,

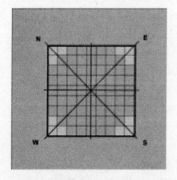
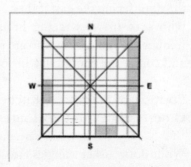

Fig. 9.11   Fig. 9.12

Gateway Positions in Mandalas

they should be located in a part or segment of the wall that allows the earth's energies to flow through. Magnetic energies flow from north to south in the northern hemisphere and vice versa in the southern hemisphere, and east to west in both hemispheres because of the rotation of the earth. Thus, if the plot is aligned cardinally, the door can be in any position in the north-east quadrant, but only in the centre in the south or the west (see Figs. 9.11 and 9.12).

As shown above, the doors in a plot or a house which is diagonal with respect to the cardinal direction, are positioned in the corners.

Toilet doors should open outwards so that they do not drain away the energies from the house or workplace, and they should be placed such that they do not obstruct the flow of energies into the plot or house as shown in the diagram.

People often subconsciously choose to live in houses with doors opening in a particular direction (north, south, east or west) depending on their aspirations, their profession and the effects that they desire from the house. As per Vaastu Shastra, people stay in houses with the door facing north if they desire wealth, happiness and prosperity; in houses with the door facing the east if they are inclined spiritually. Those who stay in west-facing houses may end up travelling frequently, and people who are primarily engaged in business and commerce should live in south-facing houses.

Position of Staircases, Kitchen, Toilets, Bedrooms and Other Utilities in the House

While doors usher energies into a space, staircases make them circulate inside and virtually carry them to the next level. Given the direction of the flow of energy in the northern hemisphere, staircases must move upwards in a clockwise direction. This was an important feature in older buildings.

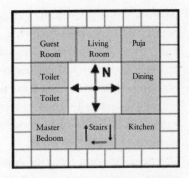

Fig. 9.13 Location of Facilities in a House

The kitchen, which houses fire, is normally located in the south-east or northwest, to harness the energies of the sun, which moves from the south-east to the north-west. The sun's energies are important for the house to provide heat and vitality to the body as well as to kill bacteria and germs.

Since fire is used to recreate and reshape objects, the south-east is also the space for creativity. Children who are creative but not short tempered can use and occupy this space.

The master bedroom, as the name implies, is meant for the master and mistress of the house. It should be located in the south-west, which is the highest and the most static part of the house. This, as per Vaastu, helps maintain the authority of and respect for parents or elders, and the relationship between them and the children. This is so because the south-west is supposed to be occupied by the decision makers and the providers of the house. Parents often tend to occupy the biggest room in the house, irrespective of the direction. When the youngsters occupy the south-west, it is often observed that they try to assert themselves which parents do not allow them to. This makes them stubborn and rebellious and causes conflict.

The north-east is also a good space for a bedroom, especially for elderly people, if more bedrooms cannot be accommodated in the south-west. The only problem is that a toilet in the north-east is an absolute no-no because the north-east is supposed to be clean, vacant and used for exalted pursuits, like prayer or studies. Toilets have drains that would drain away the energies coming in from the north-east. In this era of attached bathrooms, this creates a dilemma if a bedroom is located in the north-east. It is possible to isolate toilets energetically. In fact, we normally isolate all the toilets with copper pieces in the house and find that this results in a quantum jump in energies.

The north-west is a good corner for drawing rooms, meeting rooms, guest rooms, rooms of children studying outstation, and marriageable daughters. This area can also be used for garages and utilities like generators and washing machines.

The north wall is supposed to be the abode of Kuber, the god of wealth. Normally, Vaastu practitioners prescribe that the safe containing money or valuable documents is kept against the north wall of the room in the south-west.

Vaastu also advises that no fire-related objects such as electrical appliances, gas stoves and electrical points are located on any north wall, The same applies to drainage and water pipes. Logically speaking, since the maximum energies are generated in the north, putting drainage or fire there is like putting money or energies down the drain or on fire! In places where these are already in existence there are measures to correct such energy outflows by placing symbols.

In all countries, including Europe, houses were previously built with central courtyards and double leaf doors opening inwards to allow energies to flow in and circulate evenly within the house. Large windows let the morning sun in and high ceilings kept the interiors cool during the summer afternoons. Toilets and utility areas, including the kitchen, were located outside the house. This was done to keep the food smells and effluents out of the house and to ensure that there were no drains inside.

Centre of Plot and Building: Brahmasthanam

The centre of the plot or the house should be free of construction and preferably open to the sky. Houses were always built with a central courtyard so that the people in the house could get together. This is believed to be the place where the earth and the cosmic energies meet, coalesce and circulate throughout the house. This area in the centre of the plot, which ideally should be at least 11 per cent of the total area, is known as the Brahmhasthanam—the space of the Creator and other gods. The Central part of the building is called the Grihasthanam. The centre points of the plot and the house are Brahmanabhi and Grihanabhi, respectively.

Mythology states that in his fury, Lord Indra threw the celestial man down to the earth. He fell face downwards on to the centre of the earth and has since then, been known as the 'Vaastu Purush'. It is believed that this mythical being or force is positioned in the centre of each demarcated space, to draw in earthly and cosmic energies.

In Indian mythology, Brahma is the Creator of the universe and all life, the head of the trinity which includes Vishnu, the Preserver, and Mahesh (Shiva), the Destroyer. The concept of the holy trinity exists in numerous faiths. In Christianity, it manifests as the Father, the Son and the Holy Ghost. The point is, the centre is the sacred space where the house energies originate.

This Vaastu Purush is located in the centre of the house, and the nine points corresponding to his forehead, heart, shoulders, elbows, navel, knees and joining point of the feet are considered to be the marma points or the sensitive nodes of the plot or building. Measurements with instruments do give us nine points, which, if plotted on the plot or building plan, do somewhat seem to coincide with the body parts of the mythical person. It has been established that an

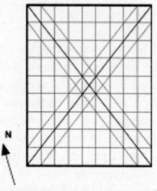

Fig. 9.14 Finding the Marma Points. When the property is at an angle to the magnetic north-south, the marma points are arrived at through a symmetrical (static) grid, which gives the best energy results.

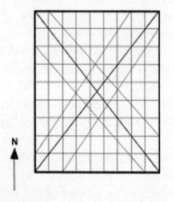

Fig. 9.15 Finding the Marma Points. When the property is parallel to the magnetic north-south, the marma points are arrived at through a non-symmetrical (dynamic) grid, which gives the best energy results.

obstruction in any of these points leads to discomfort or disease in the corresponding part of the body. Further, when these points were checked with the wavelengths of each part of the body, such as the heart or the knees, they gave positive readings. The marma points in a space can be located by dividing the length and breadth of the house into nine parts and joining these divisions for cardinally aligned and non-aligned plots or houses (see Figs. 9.14 and 9.15).

In the modern houses, it is not always possible to provide a central courtyard or even an open space. However, care should be taken to see that toilets and walls of rooms are not built in the centre of the house. Psychologically, if the centre of the house is blocked, people will tend to get isolated from one another and feel rather uncomfortable.

In the case of a built

house where the marma points are blocked by a built wall or any other type of construction, the blocked portion is energetically isolated so that it does not affect the energies of the rest of the house. This can be likened to amputating a part of the body so that the gangrene does not affect the rest of the body. Unlike amputation, however, the operation is painless and non destructive.

We tried doing a computer simulation by putting all the marma points on the floor, on the roof and all four sides of the building. We found it very interesting that this generated a mirror image pyramid which was similar to the way real ones were built, suspended in the centre of the house or the apartment. However, the marma points can be located on the floor and will take care of all the sides of this suspended shape. It has been found that if these points are energized with colours or spirals, the house or workplace energies can be considerably enhanced.

Relationship between the Human Body and a Building

The house is supposed to be an extension of the human body. In ancient times, the length and breadth of a house was a multiple of the *hasta*—the distance between the elbow of the hand and the tip of the middle finger. The *hasta* of the head of the family or the owner of the house was measured and used. In case the authority was not well defined, the dimension taken was the average of the *hastas* of all the people staying in the house.

It was believed that as the younger people in the family grew up and assumed responsibility, and the elders took on a less active role, the house should undergo some dimensional change. Its length and breadth would then become multiples of the *hasta* of the new *karta*, doer, of the family. If this was not done, the son and his family would normally settle elsewhere or if he was living in the same house, there would be discord. The dimensional change was achieved by extending a room or a part of the house, or just by building a low brick wall or plinth to redefine the contours of the house. Sometimes a patch of garden or a cluster of plants can create the desired effect.

The dimensional system in many ancient civilizations was connected with crops and the anatomy of the human body. The Indian measurement system was in multiples of eight, starting with a *parmanu*, an atom. After many multiples this went on to become a *tila*, a grain of rice. Eight *tilas* became an *angula* (width of the middle finger). The *angula* led on to the *taala* (distance between the tip of the middle finger to the base of the wrist), then to the *hasta*, *danda*, and finally the *rajju*, which is about 23 kilometres long.

Interestingly, the height of a person is usually equal to his width (fingertip to fingertip with arms outstretched horizontally). The height of a man is invariably nine times the length of his palm (*taala*), and the height of a woman, eight times the length of her palm.

Working Spaces

As in houses, the location of functions, people in offices, studios, plants and warehouses should be planned with great care. The movement of men and materials should be smooth and in the clockwise direction in the northern hemisphere. The spaces should allow circulation of air and sufficient natural light. It has been observed that if this is done, the energies of the earth and functional integrity will be well taken care of.

Production and processing spaces should be located in the

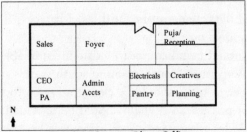

Fig. 9.16 Layout Plan: Office

south-west and south-east, if possible. North-west, the unstable zone, can be used to store finished goods, so that they do not remain in the plant or the warehouse for too long. In offices, sales personnel should be placed in the north-west, so that they remain out of the office in the field, visiting customers and selling. As in homes, in workplaces too, utilities can be installed in the north-west.

South-west, the seat of power, should be the abode of the CEO, the accounts and the administration. Raw material storage and production processes requiring heavy machines can also be situated in this quadrant. This area can also be used by decision makers and strategy planners.

The north-east is suitable for the reception, key personnel, light machinery and clean production processes.

The south-east, which is associated with creativity and fire, can be used for planning, advertising, research, server

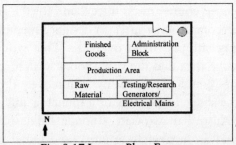

Fig. 9.17 Layout Plan: Factory

rooms, boilers, generators, utilities, furnaces, liquid fuel storage, and so on.

Care should be taken not to locate inflammable material and processes in the north-east and south-west.

The central space should be clean and open to the sky. If that is not possible, a skylight should be provided. It would be a good idea to provide a recreation area here.

Recently, we were asked to examine a large commercial building, which was almost fully constructed. The top floor was to be the office of the chairman and other senior executives and consultants of the group; the next four floors below, the offices of other companies, and the first five floors to be used by the other companies of the same group. The building was circular with a large circular central courtyard which was almost 50 per cent of the total area. The energies, even at that stage, with all construction materials and dirt lying around was very high. Our brief was to suggest layout changes for the top honcho's office, if required, which we did and these were readily accepted by the architect. In addition, we planned to rectify the radiations from magnetic grid lines, underground water streams, and other sources once the building was completed.

We complimented the accomplished and renowned architect for his design. He then told us about his most ingenuous feature. In order to create a private recreation area in the central courtyard on the ground for the employees of the group companies, a specially designed membrane canopy was being shipped from overseas. This would be fixed between the fifth and the sixth floors so that staff of other companies could not see below. Moreover, the membrane was in the shape of a vortex or a funnel facing upwards.

Our Australian associate, Rhonda Tallnash, a Feng Shui expert and an amazingly intuitive and gifted person, who was on a professional visit at our invitation, almost went into convulsions. She turned her full fury on him. 'You are trying to separate people—them and us. This is not good Feng Shui. The membrane will not let the energies flow down very freely. The funnel shape will create a strong energy vortex that will spiral upwards and cause maximum agitation for the top floor occupants'.

Not being exposed to such concepts, this assault made the architect react strongly, and he refused to remove the canopy.

We then spoke to the chairman and handed him a note on the subject. He informed us that there would be no change in their plans. Too much money had been spent. We could try to do some energetic corrections, if possible, later.

After a few months, we visited the site and found the canopy in place. It was an eyesore and a lot of dirt had accumulated on it. Our instruments showed that the energies had fallen, especially on the top floor. We once again entreated the concerned people to remove it, despite its high cost. We later learnt that the chairman also agreed that it spoilt the aesthetics of the structure. Perhaps the energies did not make him feel good. It was removed.

The point that is being made is that though buildings are often made as per Vaastu and principles of good energy, practitioners do not have the knowledge, imagination and the wherewithal to check what the energies are like, even after the building has been made.

Many Vaastu, Feng Shui and other intervention practitioners prescribe designs and solutions without actually knowing for certain whether they would have the desired effect. They do not have the ability to sense the nature and flow of energies or the instruments to check them.

Interiors

After deciding where to place the building on the plot and the location of the processes and the functions within, it is critical to plan the internal arrangement of doors, windows, and the orientation of people with care.

Doors should be positioned to ensure that they are not in line with people sitting or sleeping (see Fig. 9.18). This is because their edges emit harmful electromagnetic radiations. Similarly, people should not be seated with their backs to the windows. They literally would not know what is happening behind their backs. Windows should be positioned to provide a view. But if it is not possible to avoid a window at the back, the blinds can be closed.

As discussed earlier, working or sleeping positions must be oriented correctly with respect to the earth's magnetic flows—north and east while sitting, and head in the south and east while sleeping. Often, in open work plan offices, workstations have four people facing different directions. Two of them would naturally be incorrectly oriented. In such cases, a symbol can be worn by the person or fixed on a wall to align energies correctly.

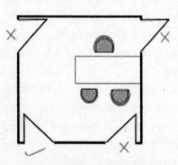

Fig. 9.18 Right & Wrong Door Positions

Masks, spears, daggers and similar artifacts and paintings that are gruesome and martial can lead to quarrels and fights within offices and homes. After masks were removed from the boardroom of a major beverage multinational, the employees reported that for the first time after they had shifted to that office, they heard laughter during a board meeting.

Magnetic Grid Lines, Underground Water Streams, Electrical Radiations

In Chapter 8, we spoke about the high negative energies emanated by the magnetic grid lines and the earth's cavities, and the need to plan buildings and their spaces to avoid negative impacts. Both, the magnetic lines and the underground cavities, can be located by instruments like the Lecher Antenna. The pattern of cracks on the walls of buildings, which are more than two to three years old, are also indicators of the location of such lines.

Electrical radiations should be avoided as far as possible. Small stickers of harmonizing colours such as those developed by Syenergy can be put on computers, switches, printers, phones, and other electrical gadgets.

Sharp edges of beams and columns also emit negative radiations, and sitting and sleeping areas should not be directly under them. Alternately, these edges should be rounded off or a curved beading should be fixed all along the sharp surface.

Feng Shui

Feng Shui, which translates as Wind and Water, is an amazingly intuitive, incisive and effective system of knowledge, which is practised to ensure well-being, wealth, happiness, and efficiency in homes and workplaces. Like Vaastu Shastra, it was derived from ancient Chinese traditions, lifestyle, land topography and symbolism. Like Vaastu, it dealt with relative heights; effects of doors and windows; harmful effects of sharp edges; importance of colours, and how they could enhance

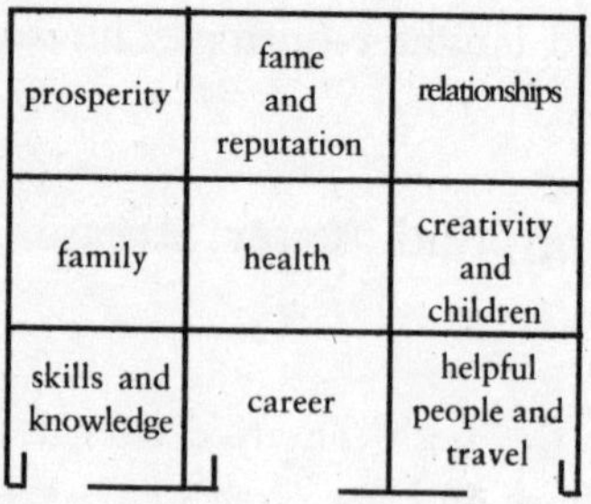

prosperity	fame and reputation	relationships
family	health	creativity and children
skills and knowledge	career	helpful people and travel

Fig. 9.19 Ba-kua Method

or depress energies in various parts of the house; use of mirrors, plants and flowers, and many other inputs.

One of the most effective ways of analysing and correcting a house is by using the *ba-kua*, an octagonal-shaped symbol of Chinese culture. A *ba-kua* is superimposed on the plan of the house with its centre coinciding with the centre of the house. The octagonal is divided into 8 triangles, starting with the one facing the entrance, which when moving clockwise, is followed by knowledge, family, wealth, fame, marriage, children, and mentors. Benefits can be derived from each of these sectors by locating a function which represents the appropriate facet in that segment, for example, having a bedroom in the family and children segment, and master bedroom in the marriage segment, a well-decorated drawing room in the fame or the wealth segment, which should also be used to house the safe. In the case of an office, the signage on the door should display the name of the company and, if possible, give an indication of its trade.

The foyer of an office should make the nature of the business of its inhabitants clear. Where it is not possible to locate appropriate functions, photographs or objects representing that function can be placed to create a virtual reality.

Feng Shui practitioners liberally prescribe the use of mirrors to virtually expand spaces and bounce back undesirable energies; the use of plants to generate positive energies, soften sharp edges and the effects of electrical radiations; while wind chimes, turtles, and other symbols are used to enhance luck, good health, and wealth, respectively.

There are various methods and practices used by different schools of Feng Shui. What is most important, however, is to have the understanding and imagination to know what would work in a particular condition and environment.

Singapore

The city of Singapore is a classic example of the judicious use of Feng Shui to create well-being and prosperity. The main boulevard, from the airport to the city, is lined with large lush trees and plants on both sides, as well as the centre. Meandering pathways on either side of the road and water bodies create gentle flows of good energy. The buildings and high rises are interspersed with greenery and water fountains. Most residential buildings and offices are rectangular in shape. Some are octagonal to correspond with the *ba-kua*. Their roofs are often triangular, the pointed roof being believed to harness cosmic energies.

Feng Shui recognizes that different people have different energies, which can be maximized in different parts of the house. Each person has a *kua* number, which is worked out from his date of birth. This decides the part of the *ba-kua* in the house where that person can be most beneficially located. On the other hand, Vaastu prescribes that the human body and its energies are universal in quality, and what is good for one is good for the other too. Unlike Vaastu Shastra, Feng Shui also does not specify particular directions or quadrants for particular functions. The functions are arranged in a house with respect to the front door. Feng Shui propagates that each house, irrespective of its environment, can create its own world, and its own virtual reality.

As mentioned earlier, the reason Feng Shui is more popular and simpler to implement is that there are many more corrections and solutions prescribed in it than in Vaastu Shastra, in the manner that it is generally practised. However, the correct understanding of the science and basis of Vaastu Shastra can lead to simple ways of correcting and enhancing energies in built structures without having to break, modify, or remake anything.

It is imperative to understand that the symbols used in China or India may not work as effectively elsewhere, especially if the meaning of that symbol is not understood or accepted. For example, the dragon is a revered animal in China but a feared one in most other parts of the world.

Public Monuments

Public monuments are not meant for living or working in. They are places where large numbers of people congregate for different purposes. Thus they have to be designed differently.

Round shapes, big open halls, high domes and ceilings are preferred in monuments. Let us examine some design facets of some ancient and modern monuments which are still visited by people and continue to inspire.

When you visit the Acropolis, in Athens, you will notice that the pillars look straight, with equal spacing between each. When a large object is viewed from a distance we see a perspective vision. This means that if we are standing at the centre, the columns to the left and right should look more closely placed together than the central columns, and as the columns go up, they should have a tapering effect. Why is this not so in the Acropolis? It was found that the columns were so constructed that they became broader with height to nullify the tapering effect. Also the outer columns were spaced farther apart from one another as compared to the central columns to make them look equidistant. The ratio of the length to the width was 1:1.614, which is the golden dimension. Many other unique features were incorporated in the planning and design. To this day, though it is completely in ruins, millions of visitors are awed and enthralled by the Acropolis. We can well imagine the effect it must have had on people when it was in its original form and splendour.

Coming to more recent structures, the Bahai Temple, in New Delhi, presents many unique features of design. Though the architects profess not to have followed any Vaastu principles, the plot has an entrance in the extended northeast. The pathways are within neutral grid lines. The lotus-shaped temple represents the nine cycles of creation and the dome inside has very high energy levels. Relative heights of structures, slopes of land, and relative placement of various buildings within the complex represent a unity of design and create a harmony within the environment.

The Sydney Opera House in Australia, is another example of a synthesis of design, material, heights, shape and acoustics. The river flowing along the southern periphery of the structure brings in good energy. This is in keeping with the belief that in the southern hemisphere, the south needs to be lower and the north higher. This monument continues to inspire and awe millions of visitors.

The building of the Indian Institute of Technology (IIT), Delhi, where I spent five years studying, was designed by Le Courbusier, the renowned French architect who designed parts of Delhi and the whole city of Chandigarh, which is the capital of two important states in India, Punjab and Haryana. The main administrative building of IIT, while being fully functional, has ramps like those which are found in galleys of ships. The architectural features at the top of the building give it the distinct look of a ship. A bell hung on top symbolizes the importance of time and discipline. The other faculty buildings are arranged around this main building like smaller flotillas, with beautiful landscaping on either side.

The Pyramids in Egypt are a reminder to all the modern geeks of science and technology that the ancients understood mathematics, the subtle energies of the planets and the earth so comprehensively that they were able to harness their power to benefit people and preserve food for years. Even though they had no accurate electronic instruments, they created shapes and relative proportions to a degree of accuracy that is impossible to achieve even today, in spite of all the instrumentation available.

The height of a pyramid divided by the base is equal to 'PI', calculated till the tenth decimal point. The centre of the pyramid, which is at one third its height, has a concentration of very high energy, almost infinite, which preserves everything that is kept within that space. It is also not common knowledge that each pyramid has an equal inverted shape which is built under the ground, almost like a mirror image.

During my visit, I checked the earth's energies around the pyramids. For almost 200 m around the circumference, the energies were very high. I was astounded to discover that the earth's magnetic lines could not be detected or measured within this radius. Thus, it was obvious that the shape and materials of the pyramid were, in conjunction, generating energies which were not only much higher than that of the earth, but which also had the power and intensity to change the nature of the magnetic flows which emanate with great force from the core of the earth. There is no evidence that any pyramid has been destroyed yet by an earthquake. No earthquake has occurred in or near places where pyramids have been built.

My friends and I were warned that anyone with even a slight breathing problem, a heart ailment, claustrophobia or any other kind of ailment should not enter the pyramids. This sounds incongruous since we hear of innumerable centres of pyramid therapy, where people are seated in the centre of artificially made pyramid-like structures to be healed. Many of those who have undergone such treatments confirm that they have been cured.

How do we reconcile these contrasting beliefs. Real pyramids were meant for dead people, not living ones. They were designed to preserve food and dead bodies for decades by crystallizing the cellular structure of the body. Living beings require constant interchange of energy, and thrive when energies flow. They cannot exist for long in inert atmospheres. However, although modern pyramids partially replicate the shape and the proportions of the ancient structures, they are built for therapy and are, therefore, not sealed. They allow ventilation and light. Some benefit does result because of the shape. I have been requested by some people to check the energies within the pyramidical structures that they have created. The results vary from disastrous to mildly beneficial. Not worth the effort and quite misleading!

Another popular practice is to use small plastic or metal pyramids liberally in houses or workplaces to energize spaces, remove negative energies, improve health or bring luck. Our tests have demonstrated that nothing can be more hazardous or undesirable. Only one in ten seem to have a salubrious effect on the surroundings and the people around.

This is because pyramid shapes radiate very strong energies. They therefore have to be carefully placed so that they are in harmony with and maximize the energies around. Improper use can create discordant and clashing energies that can harm people. Ninety-nine out of a hundred people do not know how to use them. Therefore, my suggestion is, admire them, see and study them, but do not sit inside them or make them sit in your houses.

Corrections with Plants, Colours and Other Means

We know that while it is easy to talk about the right way to build structures, and to orient people in them as well as to allocate the correct spaces for them to use, it is often not possible to fulfil all these requirements. Most town planners have created plots and colonies which are diagonal to the cardinal directions. They have positioned entry gates incorrectly and it is often not possible to choose the direction which you should face or the slope of land that is desirable. Most people either buy or rent workplaces which are already constructed, thereby having no say in the construction aspect. In this scenario, what is to be done?

While a complete correction and enhancement of energies can be done by knowledgeable practitioners who work in a professional and scientific manner, it is often possible to implement some corrective measures ourselves, which can greatly enhance the energies and create a good atmosphere for living and working in. These include the position of doors, correction of sharp edges, treating electrical radiations, avoiding magnetic grid lines and orienting ourselves correctly. Here are a few other suggestions and ways by which we can help ourselves:

1. Plot shape
If the plot is not square or rectangular, we can make it so by cutting off the extra portion with a line of lime, or a single line of brickwork (see Figs. 9.20 and 9.21).

2. Missing corners

If the corner of a house or a plot is missing, we can complete the corner by again drawing a line with lime or brick-mortar. If this is not possible, we can put a mirror on the wall in front of the corner so that the existing space is doubled and is projected into the missing portion.

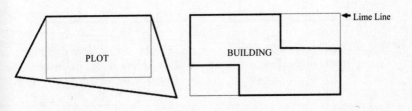

Fig. 9.20   Fig. 9.21
Converting Plots to Rectangular Shapes

3. Toilets

Toilets need to be isolated energetically. Feng Shui prescribes putting a mirror in front of the toilet door to reflect back the energies into the house so that they do not enter the toilet. Crystallization of toilets or putting mirrors on all sides of the toilet is also prescribed sometimes to confine the energies of the toilet within itself. This, of course, is not generally practical or feasible to implement. However, in the bedrooms, mirrors should not face one another.

4. Wrong position of entrances

We can correct the flows of these entrances by putting a Swastika, clockwise spiral or image of Ganesha on either side of the door exactly half way from the bottom to the top (see Fig. 9.23), or putting the same on top of the door exactly in the centre of the opening (see Fig. 9.22).

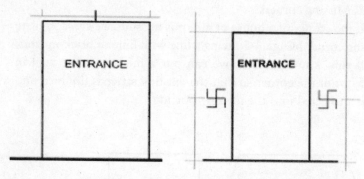

Fig. 9.22 Ganesh image at the top centre of the door

Fig. 9.23 The Swastika on either side of the door, halfway from bottom to top

5. Colours

House energies can be corrected by using eight colours in the eight cardinal and diagonal corners of the house as described in detail in the chapter on colours. This is a simple method of correcting and enhancing energies within a room or an entire building.

While painting a building, the use of bright colours in light pastel shades creates an atmosphere of joy and vivacity, whereas dull grey and brown would induce boredom and inactivity. Glossy surfaces are preferred in indoor spaces where abundant natural light is not available and matt finishes are preferred for outer walls so that they absorb heat and light and do not reflect them on those approaching, thereby making them uncomfortable.

6. Use of plants

Plants can be used to soften the effect of sharp edges and minimize the effect of negative electrical radiations. Of course, care should be taken not to keep cacti, dried flowers, dead leaves and plants as they create and give rise to want, deprivation and decay. Money plants, which are very popular and can be found in almost every house are diseased plants, which affect the nervous system, and enhance stress, and should be kept away from the house and the plot.

7. Ceiling heights
Avoid low ceilings as they literally create pressure and increase your blood pressure. The most important correction is to keep your house clean and have minimum storage. Look at all that you have collected over the years. Only keep what is absolutely necessary for now and not something, which you may need tomorrow, or you may like to look at some day. Throw or give away the rest. Then try to halve what is left behind. Clutter in the house or in the workplace creates clutter in life and in our minds.

8. Light A Candle
'Light a candle and bring happiness into your life.' No truer statement has ever been made. Do this in the centre of the house and see the difference it makes to your life and health. Care should be taken that only one candle or an odd number of candles burn inside a house.

9. Salt water
Occasionally clean the floors of the house with water mixed with rock salt. This dispels negative energies.

10. Light and air
Allow light and fresh air to come in. Switch off your airconditioners occasionally, even at the risk of allowing some dust in. The glass clad high rise architectural marvels being built all over are an environmental nightmare. They re-

circulate stale air further polluted by room fresheners and consume too much electricity for cooling the trapped heat inside.

Conclusion

Homes and work spaces need to be selected, built, furnished and used with careful thought, care and love. They need to be maintained and looked after as we would look after our own body, our health, our elders and our children.

They can be modified and their energies can be enhanced manifold. More than professional help to select the right spaces, we need to use our intuition and our sensitivity to choose the right abodes and to use them efficiently and with love and reverence. A well-adorned house will look after you well, whereas a neglected one can only lead you to despair and ill health.

10

The Vibrations of Sound and Music

From stillness within
  A tremor—a vibration
    Is born.
To give sound and shape
  To thought and feeling.
The power of which
  takes us beyond
    Mountains and Seas.
Its soul gives life to Earth
  spurs seeds to bear
    stems and leaves,
      fruits and flowers
        better and faster
And ferrets out joy
  From the subterranean depths
    Of our hearts
With the perfect rendition
  Of love and devotion.
Finally, as the sound subsides
  Consciousness ascends.

When a child is born, people do not smile or celebrate till they hear the first wail or the first sound. A whisper can be heard miles away whereas a shout may not be heard in the same room. The same words from two different people can either sound like music or jar at our whole being—they can sound like music to one and noise to another. Sound can move people and mountains—such is its power and versatility. A single note of music can stir the quietest emotion within our soul and hear what we have not heard before, and an inaudible sound can make us deaf.

My earliest recollection of music goes back to sitting on my father's lap. Being blessed with both an ear and appreciation for music, he bought dozens of long playing and 78 rpm records every month. His collection included classical and film music, cha-cha-cha and rock and roll. Even though he was never formally trained, he could recognize the raga on which a song was based, pick up the beat and understand the nuances of the compositions. I remember crawling to the stack of discs, feeling them with my hands and remembering the songs by the scratches and marks on them, some of which I made, when I could find none. I am told that I could hum before I could speak and sing before I could read and write. Music, prayer and sports, formed the trinity of my being and existence.

Music can uplift our consciousness. If properly rendered, it awakens within us the spirit of prayer, compassion and love. It clears our minds. Music sings our blues away. It lets the child within us play and the adult in us work and create. Music has the power and the ability to captivate our mind, soothe our hearts, resurrect our spirit and transform our being. The fact that it forms an important part of our living experience is apparent. Terms commonly used by us such as, 'communicate on the same wavelength', 'strike a sympathetic chord', and 'set the right tone', illustrate this vividly.

The Power of Sound

Sound is vibration which has a certain frequency and wavelength. If it is emitted in a way that it resonates with the vibratory frequency of another object, it can make the object move or change its form and shape. There is the story of Joshua, who took a small army led by seven priests blowing trumpets, and destroyed the mighty walls of Jericho, without firing a single shot. When he was approaching the city, he encountered a sage, who advised him to use sound in sequences of seven. He told him to get seven priests to march around the walls for seven days, seven times during a day, blow the trumpets seven times and take seven steps in unison with sharp sounds. They did so, and lo and behold! the walls fell. Archaeological evidence confirms that the walls fell outwards, not inwards, which would have been the case if force was used from outside. We have already given a detailed chart showing the relevance of seven musical notes, planets, colours, symbols, chakras, gems and their association with one another and to elements and many other things known to us.

Indian history recounts how the rendition of a raga—a combination of notes, sung at the right pitch and tone, helped bring about rain in a drought-affected area. A disciple of Tansen, the legendary maestro at the court of the famous Mughal emperor Akbar, sang a raga called Megh Malhar to invoke rain and give life and succour to the entire populace.

This fact, like many other amazing feats that occurred during the existence of earlier civilizations, was consigned to the dustbin of folklore, myth and superstition. It is now admitted and accepted that this phenomenon was entirely feasible if the power and purity of sound was high. Sounds and combinations of notes emitted at a certain pitch are now used to cause precipitation of clouds by changing their molecular structure.

Former civilizations, especially the pre-Christian ones, were aware of the power of music. The people of China, India, Egypt and Greece believed that there was something immensely fundamental about music: it had the power to not only sublimely evolve or utterly degrade individuals, but even entire civilizations. They understood that music could unite or destroy nations.

When we are within the audible range of music, our heartbeat, nerves, blood pressure, digestion and breathing are affected. When music is internalized, it affects the rhythm of our thoughts, the melody of emotion, the harmony of health and the structure of bodily poise.

As in Music, So in Life

Yehudi Menuhin, the most reputed violinist of our times, writes: 'Music creates order out of chaos, for unity imposes unanimity upon the divergent; melody imposes continuity upon the disjointed, and harmony imposes compatibility upon the incongruous.

'Thus confusion surrenders to order and noise to music, and as we through music attain that greater universal order which rests upon fundamental relationships of geometric and mathematical proportion, direction is supplied to repetitious time, power to multiplication of elements and purpose to random association.'

Aristotle, the great Greek philosopher, believed that music had the power to form character. He believed that emotions are produced by melody and rhythm.

Pythagoras, the master mathematician and thinker, said that all music can be reduced to numbers or mathematical ratios—the universe and all its phenomena could be explained by them.

Einstein was inspired by the mystical experiences brought about by music. It helped him, in no small measure, in developing the theory of quantum physics and to propose that matter was nothing but vibration.

Yo Ki (Memorial of Music), the most important Chinese text on sound and music, states, 'Under the effect of music, the five social duties are without admixture, the eyes and ears are clear, the blood and vital energies are balanced. Habits are reformed, customs are improved and the empire is at complete peace.'

Today, music is often regarded as a non-essential and a peripheral aspect of human life. Children are told that delving in music is a good hobby, but should not be treated too seriously. It can be a diversion, not the prime occupation. Parents and relatives are often worried about children who spend long hours listening to or practising music. They feel that the child is not focused and serious about life and is wasting time.

Our ancients would have been anguished to see this change in attitude and orientation. They believed that music was the most intrinsic and essential part of our being. In the hands of the evil, it could lead to doom and destruction. When guided by spiritual and evolved people, it could make nations and civilizations powerful and prosperous.

The kinds of music heard by a mother when her child is in her womb are known to significantly impact the mental development of the child. Mozart's music, which is known to be mathematically ingenuous, is known to enhance mathematical ability. I am told by my mother that she was made to hear devotional songs when she was carrying me, whereas, being more free willed by then, she heard peppy and romantic songs when my sister was in her womb.

As a child, I wanted to listen to music all the time, even while I was studying. I was mesmerized and enthralled by the way notes flirted, melded with, entwined and followed one another. A good composition has that power, it comprises a few combinations that surprise us and take our breath away—similar to our encountering a breathtaking view as we round a corner or take a turn. I would often hear music without it being actually played. This music was not a recollection of something that I had heard before; it was new and unfamiliar, yet natural and beautiful. I would also see images and shapes, which would change constantly with the notes of the sound. I did not know how to share my experiences with friends without being ridiculed. Neither did I dare to do so with my elders, in spite of the fact that many of them were musically inclined. I started believing that what was happening to me was not normal or rational, and consequently, consciously shut it out, thus losing the felicity and grace to see and hear much more than what I can hear today.

I am happy and relieved that I have moved towards rediscovering the bliss and the spirituality of music and, consequently, the most important parts of myself I had lost. My inner music has helped me tide over prolonged periods of difficulties without becoming cynical and suspicious about life and people.

The Learning of Music

In India and most of Asia and medieval Europe, the learning of music and other arts and sciences was imparted in gurukuls and monasteries, learning centres where teacher and pupil stayed together for years. Before beginning instruction and training in the chosen vocation, the pupil was made to do all sorts of chores to develop humility and compassion, and given lessons to differentiate between good and bad, right and wrong. These, along with prayer and lessons to develop spiritual understanding, continued throughout his stay. It was believed that it was more important for a musician or scientist to be a good human being instead of merely being a virtuoso or intellectually clever.

A famous Zen story illustrates this well. A student went to a Zen master to learn fencing. The master agreed to teach him on condition that he would never question him on his methods of teaching or anything else. For almost two years, he made him clean his house, cook food, tend to the garden and feed the animals. The young man finally mustered up courage to ask him when he was going to start his lessons.

The master was livid. He reminded the pupil about his promise about not asking any question. He warned him that if he did so again, he would ask him to leave. The master asked him to go back to his old routine. One day, when he was cutting the shrubs, the master attacked him from behind. A few days later, he did so again while the young man was cooking. Subsequently, the student was constantly on guard. When attacked, he turned around and defended himself. The master proclaimed that the boy had learnt to be alert all the time and he would now teach him fencing.

Ustad Allaudin Khan, a venerated teacher, would lock up his son, Ustad Ali Akbar Khan, the internationally famous *sarod* wizard, and Pandit Ravi Shankar, the world-renowned sitar maestro, for twelve to fourteen hours in a bare room to practise. Often, a pupil was made to practise the same raga for years till he mastered all the nuances and variations. A few years ago, a friend of mine, Anmol Vellani, president of Ford Foundation, India, confirmed to me that he had formally learnt one raga, Chandrakaus, for the past five years. The most famous musicians, even today, take pride in associating themselves with a *gharana*, a house of music, which has preserved and passed on a lineage of a particular style and nuance of singing for hundreds of years. It is customary for a singer to precede a performance with a silent prayer and invoking the blessings of his or her guru or teacher. A pupil was only allowed to perform in public after the guru deemed him ready and fit to do so. This could sometimes take 10-20 years.

The Origins of Sound

The ancients were aware that audible sound is nothing but the earthly reflection of the cosmic vibration. This vibration is inaudible to the human ear, but is the origin and basis of all matter and energy in the universe. The purest vibration is Om. It is not *a* sound, it is *the* sound. It is not one of the creations of the universe, it is the universe. Om diffuses into a number of more well-defined super physical vibrations. These cosmic tones, called *shrutis* in India and *lui* in China, are closer in vibration to the tangible, physical world. Astrology is based on these cosmic tones. The twelve signs of the zodiac correspond to the twelve tones. The Egyptions called them the 'Word of the Gods'; the Greeks—the 'Music of the Spheres'. Across civilizations, this sound was held in great reverence.

In other civilizations too, the phenomena of a primal sound was known and developed. The Christians call it Amen, the Greeks—Logos, the Persians—Ameen. The Jews chant Yahuvahah, and the Egyptian equivalent is Amn. The Chinese called this sound Huang-Huang and the musical note, Kung.

The Upanishads, the most comprehensive knowledge treatise of ancient Indian civilizations, which dealt with all forms and aspects of creation—life, food, aspirations and behaviour, as well as Chinese texts stated that this form of vibration was the source of all the forces in the universe, including light and the entire electro-magnetic spectrum. Modern speculation has established that ultrasonic sound vibrating a glass rod causes the rod to emanate both heat and light.

St. John says, 'In the beginning there was the Word, and the Word was with God, and the word was God. All things were made by Him, and without Him was not anything that was made'.

The Science of Creation, Matter and Sound

According to the grand unified theory of physics, electricity, magnetism and heat are different aspects of the same energy and interchangeable with one another and with gravity too! Thus, gravity can be converted into heat or light, making levitation possible, or we can create gravity from electricity. This suggests that energy can be transferred from higher planes to the physical or material plane, enabling us to tap infinite sources of unlimited energy and make things materialize or dematerialize.

The fascinating experiments by Dr Hans Jenny, a Swiss scientist and artist, followed by those of Dr Ernst Chladni in establishing the science of Cymatics—the study of form, shapes and patterns in various mediums, show us the unbelievable shapes and changing patterns made by single notes and combinations of notes. Dr Tomatis, a French scientist, sprinkled dust particles or iron filings on a taut rubber membrane or cloth fixed to a long funnel-shaped instrument, called the Tonoscope, to form and change patterns with musical notes. The rendition of Om forms a 108-sided lotus. A good musical composition forms beautiful visuals in water or air. Dancing forms in air and water can be filmed. At airports and metro railway station platforms, pictures of water visuals formed by sound are admired by and bring down the stress levels of thousands of commuters.

So what did we do with this discovery other than marvel at it? Quite a bit! It was and is used for curing deaf-mute people who are encouraged to observe the patterns formed by vowels of normal people and replicate them till they can get the right sound and learn to speak. More than 1,00,000 people have visited listening centres in different parts of the world to get treated.

Einstein and many other scientists and quantum physics have firmly established that solidity of matter is an illusion. Substances are formed out of millions of minute atoms, which are separated from each other by large distances. Within the atom, the size of an electron circling around the nucleus is the size of a dust speck in a football field. The electron, when examined under powerful microscopes, shows a few streamers floating around. They are nothing but energy in motion. Moreover, it was discovered that atoms have resonance. They themselves are tiny musical notes. Hans Kruger found that the structure of the atom contains ratios and numbers similar to the harmonic principles of music. A note, if it can be played 40 octaves higher, will not be heard but seen as pure light! Vibratory activity at a frequency of 6,00,000 waves per second is sensed by our eyes and transmitted to the brain as the visual perception of light and colour. The seven notes on the musical scale correspond to the seven VIBGYOR colours, the seven chakras of the subtle body, seven planets, seven gems, and so on. They have the ability to transmute to a different form with a suitable change in octaves. When a note is sung, we can often feel the vibration in the corresponding chakra of the body or visualize the corresponding colour.

The following figure shows the entire spectrum of electro-magnetic waves. It can be seen that visible light occupies only one-seventieth of this spectrum.

All electromagnetic waves move in spiral flows. Blood moves through the veins in waves; air and water also travel in waves. Matter is the warp and weft of sound. The mystics recognized that our own body and consciousness is the manifestation of the word and we have the ability and the sacred responsibility to invoke and transmit the energy of Om—the word, to all life by silent meditation or audible sound. Incidentally, church bells and *shankhas*, spiral-shaped blowing conches, do the same. 'Om' has the ability to change the vibratory frequency and amplitude of the body, rejuvenate dead cells, cure disease and help us attain higher states of consciousness.

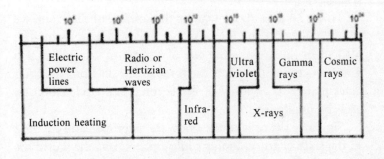

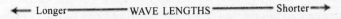

Fig. 10.1 Spectrum of Electromagnetic Waves

The seven colours, crystals—rock and mineral, organs, chakras, hormonal glands, ventricles and cavities of the skull are cubic, rhombohedral, hexagonal, triclinic, monoclinic, trigonal and orthorhombic in shape.

Harry Kayser discovered that the relation of ratios in atomic physics, astronomy, botany and architecture is the same. He discovered that the deep sea is filled with harmonic sounds.

Fritzof Capra, in his book, *The Tao of Physics*, illustrates how forms are associated with processes. Since matter at sub-atomic levels consists of changing energy patterns, he suggested that we need to shift our focus from structure to rhythm. The ecosystem, civilization, planets and our world have their cycles of activity and rest—they vibrate in harmonic proportions.

Planck's Constant is a formula that states when a photon moves at the speed of light, its mass is zero and it occupies no space. This makes the phenomena of materialization of an object or a person placed or present at one place at another location not only sound feasible, but almost normal and scientific.

To get an idea about what is the solidity of the atom, we can imagine that the Empire State building is an atom. The nucleus of the atom is the size of a grain of salt within this huge structure. So what is the force or the phenomenon that gives matter its solidity? It is the force of sound, vibration and the oscillations.

Similarly the cells of the body are emptiness and rhythm. In the sixth century, Indian philosophers gave the world the concept of zero without which modern mathematics and science cannot survive. Asian thought conceived of the concept of *Shunyata*—void. The pearl of Lord Indra, the God of Wealth, contains and represents all other pearls in the world.

Nuclear physics was to discover much later that any electron of a single atom contains all the nuclear secrets of the world. When the programming of a microchip is changed, it is known that all other microchips which are exactly the same would get automatically reprogrammed.

When we talk of holography, it is nothing else except photography with laser waves. A photograph taken thus cannot be divided. If done, the full picture is formed again.

What does all this have to do with music?

Every musical note is based on a mathematical concept. As mentioned earlier the octave of the musical scale corresponds to planetary distances. It also corresponds to the proportions of the human body. The proportions of the sixth octave 3:5, 5:8, 8:13, 13:21 correspond to the golden section: $A:B = B:(A-B)$. The eyebrow divides the head; the knee divides the leg; the elbow divides the arm, and the navel—the whole body, in similar ratio.

Mantras

According to the Rig Veda, mantras are archetypal word symbols; they are pre-lingual and convey feelings, not concepts, emotions or ideas. They originate from *bijas*, seeds, which sprout oneness and become tools for hearing Om. Particle physics has proposed that the elements of a single electron contains all the nuclear secrets of the world. The scriptures, both Eastern and Western, refer to the the holy trinity of creation: Brahma or the Father—the Creator who is also all creation or the Brahman; Vishnu or the Son, the Perpetuator; and Shiva or the Holy Ghost, the Destroyer who enables fresh creation, new life and resurrection.

The Japanese use *koans*, questions or statements to dwell upon, while the Chinese use *tao*, where the question can be the answer. Both these are powerful tools for attaining a higher state of consciousness, like the mantras. The Indians believe that the name of a person is the mantra of the person's aspirations which can be realized with minimal effort. When someone mentioned this to me a few years ago, I pondered over it and realized that I had faced many difficult situations but had never given up or felt defeated or helpless. My name, Ajay, or Ajeya, means one who cannot be defeated, or one who will overcome and be victorious. Internalizing the meaning has strengthened my resolve and focus.

Certain sounds or vowel combinations were used to create effects and express emotions. For example, AH expresses wonder, direct awareness, praise and adoration, and is a sound of love and satisfaction. HUM causes the descent of universality into the human heart. AUM causes the ascent towards universality and HRIH kindles the upward spiralling flame of aspiration and devotion.

A very powerful ritual which is still performed at many homes, during weddings and important social gatherings is the *hawan*, lighting a fire in a inverted pyramid-shaped vessel or a pit dug in the ground with offerings of oil, food, wood, while intoning and reciting shlokas. One such *hawan*, which is known as the Agnihotra, is performed before sunrise. It is known that the earth's energy is rising before the sun rises. That is why the fragrance of flowers and the earth is strongest at night and till dawn. The words or mantra intoned are '*Om Surya swaha, Suryaye idam namah, Om prajapataya swaha, prajapataya idam namah*.' The smoke and particles are known to rise almost 23 km above the ground and then descend like a cloud into the atmosphere and the earth. This descending cloud charges the negative ions, which are beneficial for the body. It is also beneficial for crops and reduces pollution levels and incidence of high blood pressure and cancer. Dr Vasant Papanjpe, who has his ashram in Maheshwar, on the banks of the Narbada river, which, like the Ganga, is revered by millions in India, has made this ritual very popular in Latin America. It is also known as Homa farming.

Music raises the vibratory frequency of the body to transform matter into spirit. The Vedas were not read but intoned and sung, as are hymns, to release wisdom as sacred energy.

The Bija Mantras, which are also primal sounds believed to have originated from Om, create a harmonic resonance with the elements and our body – Lam with Earth, Vam with water, Yam with air, Ram with fire and Ham with ether. Each of these correspond with the chakras of the body and their surrounding areas. For example, a sore throat can be cured by intoning 'Ham'.

My sister, Shruti, who is a vedic scholar and a musician, teaches the intonation of the Bija mantras and AUM. She claims that she has not taken a pill or medicines for the last fifteen years and people have been cured listening to her cassettes of the Bija Mantra and AUM.

Music and the Planets

Johannes Kepler, the famous astronomer, found that the vibrations of our vowels correspond to the planets—A to Jupiter, I to Mars, O to Venus, U to Saturn and E to Mercury. Planets chime like gigantic musical instruments and can induce resonance and harmonics in each other. In 1766, Titius found that all planets known to astronomers in his day possessed mean orbital distances from the innermost planet, Mercury. Earth was twice as far from its orbit as compared to Venus, Mars twice as far compared to Earth, Jupiter twice the distance of Mars, and so on. This is exactly as per the ratio of octaves—each succeeding note is twice the distance from the distance between the preceding two. Solar vibrations are audible to the human ear. Quiet whizzing, hissing, crackling and hissing sounds can sometimes be heard. The Northern Lights is a phenomenon visible from Canada and Norway which is accompanied by an unusual sound.

The Creation of Music

The known origins of music and compositions go back to 3000 BC in China. The five wise monarchs, starting with Fu Hsi, created a system of learning and rendition of sound to preserve the unity and well-being of the nation and its people. In the sixteenth century, when Emperor Shun toured the regions of the country, neither did he check the books of accounts nor did he review the work of the authorities. What then did he do? He checked the exact pitches of the notes that they played and the tuning of their instruments. Eight kinds of Chinese instruments were played before him. The wise man firmly believed that if the instruments in different regions were tuned differently, there would be discord and chaos. He also heard folk songs and the tunes sung in the court and checked whether they corresponded to the five notes of the ancient Chinese musical scale.

In Eastern civilizations, it was believed that each rhythm was a prayer and every melody a contemplation. They gave great importance to ceremony. Confucius stated that ceremony established the correct manner of physical movement and music perfected the mind and emotion. It was believed that music and ceremony together attuned people to the heavens. During the Tang dynasty, for one ceremony, fourteen orchestras comprising 500-700 musicians each, performed at the same time. For the most important festivals, the size of the orchestra could be as large as 10,000 musicians! Imagine the seats of a large auditorium occupied by musicians, while the stage would seat the august audience! It was felt that the larger the orchestra, the greater would be the amount of cosmic energy invoked and radiated.

For everyone who learnt to play or hear music, hearing each individual note or tone was more important than the composition. It was like seeing each line in a painting or visualizing the stroke of the brush. Today, we do not listen to the notes of music at all—we hear their combination in the form of a melody. Technically, we only hear the rise and fall of pitch differences.

In the Indian and Tibetan chants of hymns and mantras, only three notes, namely, Ti, Do and Re; Ni, Sa and Re are used, respectively. The repeated use of the same notes and the overtones around them create amplification and a resonance of the vibratory frequency of all our cells with the immediate surroundings and the higher consciousness. As mentioned earlier, all matter is rhythm. The nucleus of an atom is a reference point. As we come closer to it, it begins to dissolve and can only be observed as an oscillating field.

The Decline of Music

When and how did music get dissipated and destroyed? In China, it is believed that the acceptance of Western musicians as professors in the imperial court and the introduction of Western instruments by the Ch'ing monarchs, caused the first aberration. However, traditional music and its power prevailed. In 1912, the imperial house which had governed China for 5000 years, was overthrown and replaced by the republic. In the modern republic, in schools, factories, and villages, children and adults were encouraged to sing anti-capitalist songs and 'death chants'—rhythmic, full-throated shouts for death and destruction of people in the west. To the ancients, this would have appeared to be the practice of black magic on an international scale! In India, the first assault of music took place by the Mughal emperors who provided great patronage to music, but used it for titillation and entertainment. Music started to move away from temples to palaces, and devotional singers were replaced by courtesans.

The advent of the British further eroded and denigrated our traditions. They created a class of civil servants who aped them and encouraged their children to speak their language, hear and sing their songs. Following Indian traditions, imbibing our own culture and learning our own music was propagated by Indians themselves to be a sign of backwardness. Our national anthem, which is sung to this day, was a paen composed by our national poet, Sri Rabindranath Tagore, to welcome King George V when he set foot on our land in 1905. It goes thus: 'Jana gana man, adhinayak jaya he, Bharat bhagya vidhata'—Hail the king or lord of the masses, the arbitrer of the fate of India. One wonders why the wise decision makers of India did not change the national anthem after the country achieved independence!

Subsequently, film music, the Indian interpretation of the cha-cha-cha and now, Bhangra pop and remixes are sounding the final death knell.

The Purpose of Music

The purpose of music was not only to relax or entertain or to stimulate, but to help us attain a higher spiritual consciousness. Music was devotional and was sung individually as a form of meditation and prayer, and collectively in temples, churches and monasteries to invoke well-being and elevate us to a higher state of consciousness. The purpose of music was not to evoke normal emotions, but sublime ones.

Till the end of the nineteenth century, and even till well into the twentieth century, the purpose of music, though not overly religious, was to spread joy and brotherhood. The works of Bach, Beethoven and, of course, the most sublime genius of our times, Mozart, bear ample testimony to this. Their music had a spiritual effect though none of them were religious. Their music directed our attention not into the world, but above it. The movement was upwards and not horizontal or downwards.

'New Music'

The advent of 'new music' started with the ascent of materialism as the new mantra of life. Materialism is an exclusionist philosophy where being like others is considered a demotion. We are better if we dress better or differently, look different, have more than others. We are different, and alone. The music that we hear also has to be different, crazier, louder and more complex.

Contemporary music has directed our consciousness to the physical level. Composers started concentrating on technical innovations, virtuosity without bothering about melody and emotional content. Tchaikovsky(1840-1893), a master of melody, composed beautiful tunes. However, his last few symphonies were laced with pessimism and failure because he allowed the torment of his personal life as a homosexual to pervade his music. We find, almost unerringly, that the music made by people is a reflection of their nature and state of being. Igor Stravinsky, who is often regarded as the guru of new music, composed for six decades. *The Rites of Spring*, his most famous work, is pagan, wild, aggressive. The melodies and harmonics frighten and disrupt the mind.

Jazz, Blues and Rock started in the ghettos. They were initially sung in sleazy bars. The words were lewd and full of tribal African slang words. They often mirrored lust, frustration and violence. Most of their exponents lived short, debased, violent lives. Of course, these music forms gained acceptability and moved to the dining rooms and fancy ballrooms. Rendered by respectable and well-dressed musicians, Jazz and Blues moved into the avant-garde space to make way for Rock and Pop.

The Rolling stones, the Beatles and many other famous groups gained immense popularity with a generation of youngsters in the 1960s. That was a time when capitalism was riding high and children missed the love and care of their parents who were too busy partying or working to bother even when their children, being emotionally deprived, took to drugs and casual sex. The words and the tunes of the music promised freedom, encouraged rebellion and idolized vagabonds.

Modern music is meant to provoke, activate and titillate, and works more on our lower being than our higher consciousness. The beat emanated by Rock and Pop music is irregular and upsets the rhythm of our heartbeat. A young person who listens to Rock or Pop music for two to three hours a day is likely to have a higher heartbeat than one who does not, even when he is not listening. Teenagers often take eggs to Rock concerts. The Rock music played on stage can harden an egg like a fully boiled one within fifteen minutes. If it can do that to an egg, imagine what it does to our insides!

Famous contemporary musicians are icons for the young. They are rich, live life in the fast lane, marry and divorce frequently. They compose for and crave fame and wealth. If we observe people dancing in a discotheque, we will notice, not surprisingly, that the maximum movement of the body is at the pelvic region. Our desires are aroused and the adrenal rises. A few drinks take us to another zone. We are on fire. Soon the place lights up with brawls.

Music and Plants

Plants have been known to wither if subjected to the continuous playing of Rock music. Contrarily, if subjected to classical music played by Mozart or Bach or Ravi Shankar, they grow faster and bigger.

As stated earlier, music raises the vibratory frequency of the body to transform matter into spirit.

Ragas

The raga, an Indian concept of notes and tonal combinations, was created around 400 BC. The raga is not prearranged and structured but is developed by the artist according to his emotion and imagination, consciousness and purity. It has a predominant ascending note, which is called the *vadi* and a descending note, the *samvadi*. The artist is free to innovate within the broad structure of a raga, which is inviolate. The raga conforms to time cycles and seasons. It has a *laya*—melody, and *tala*—rhythm, and the time intervals or units are known as mantras. The initial exposition of the raga is known as the *alaap*, which is slow and languid; it focuses on the melody variation and highlights the virtuosity of the artist. The *tan* is faster, has more rhythm, percussion and energy. Within India itself, northern India is more influenced by the musical traditions of Persia and Afghanistan whereas music in southern India has remained more traditional.

Indian music differs from Western and Chinese music. The intervals between the notes are much smaller than in Western music. While Chinese music focuses on one note, Indian music lingers in the spaces between the notes. These features make it more melodious and contemplative.

Hearing and Measuring Sound

When do we start hearing? We know that the first distinguishable organ of the child that is formed in a mother's womb is the ear (within twenty-four weeks). We hear sounds that our mother hears; we listen when she talks to us. The sound is filtered through the fluid in the embryo and therefore sounds quite unlike the real sound. The quality of sound in the embryo is rich. That is the real sound for the child. The newborn hears what he or she cannot relate to, and cries. It takes time for the child to learn to 'hear' the new language when he/she comes into the world and then speak. His eyes are closed at the time of birth. Vision also becomes a reality only after birth. Many healing centres around the world are filtering spoken words and sentences by eliminating low frequencies, and simulating the sounds that the child hears in the womb to treat severe health conditions and psychological disorders in adults, with astounding success. Diseases like epilepsy have been cured.

Sound travels in waves, frequencies and intensities. It can be organized into shapes, patterns and mathematical proportions. The unit that measures frequency, the number of cycles per second, is the hertz. What we can hear depends more on the frequency and pitch, the quality of sound, than the loudness or volume of sound. In Africa, a whisper can be heard more than 90 feet away. The normal ear can hear between 16-20,000 hertz. The sound of the piano ranges from 27.5-4186 hertz. Extensive observations have established that 3000-8000 hertz affects cognitive functions like thinking and memory; above 750 hertz stimulates the heart, lungs and emotions; 125-750 hertz affects physical movement.

The most widely used unit for recording the volume of sound is the decibel, named after Bell, its inventor. The unique feature of this unit is that its scale is logarithmic. Eleven is double of ten, 110 is ten times higher than 100. Leaves rustle at 10 decibels; whispers are heard at 30 decibels, conversations at 60. Normal traffic records 70 decibels, motorcycles—100, saws—10, rock music and car horns–115, and rocket launches–180. Health is endangered after 90 decibels, and at 125 decibels, pain is experienced in the human ear.

Air vibrations are capable of shattering glass. Research into lower frequency sound has found that they can, even when they are inaudible, cause nausea and headaches. Sound from machinery also causes similar effects. Animals pick up subatomic vibrations hours before earthquakes occur. Armies break the rhythm of their marching before they cross bridges as the vibrations generated by rhythmic marching can make them collapse.

In cities, the biggest pollutants are noise and sound. In cities like Mumbai and New York, people speak very loudly even when they are near one another. Loud noise and music also make people aggressive in urban areas. The riot police is always at hand when a rock band is playing as violence breaks out in such congregations quite frequently. The morning after a night out at the discotheque, a person seems to be hard of hearing. In gymnasiums, younger people normally want the music to be played louder. Others find it to be an assault on their senses to be subjected to this kind and level of sound early in the morning, and many, therefore, prefer yoga and walking.

Doctors are finding that a very high number of people with impaired hearing are very young. The Environment Protection Agency in America is concerned about the fact that many more young people suffer from hearing problems than those in their fifties and sixties.

Our hearing determines how we speak. If we hear people around us speaking softly, we do so too. It is well known that people are normally both deaf and dumb: when they cannot hear, they cannot speak. As our hearing gets impaired when we grow, we speak slowly or the words start slurring.

The Chinese concept of Yin and Yang governs sounds and musical notes too. The six Yin notes correspond to the first six months of the year and the Yang to the last six months. Women's voices are pitched higher than men's. The sounds from violins, flutes and trumpets are Yin sounds, whereas the sounds from cellos and basses are Yang sounds. These always accompany the Yin instruments. The ear is female and more emotional and intuitive, whereas the eye is male and rational. The ears see when the eyes are closed.

Healing with Music

All illness and disease were regarded by the ancients as musical problems. Primitive societies and tribes, even now, use chants and ritual dances more than medicinal herbs to cure. This was instititionlized by the ancient Chinese, Indian, Greek and Egyptian civilizations. Hippocrates, the 'Father of Medicine', used to take his patients to the Temple of Aescupalis to listen to music and get healed. Till the Roman Empire was Christianized, priests and physicians used music therapy. Till the thirteenth century, Arab hospitals had music therapy rooms. Even today, a small number of private practitioners are using music therapy to great effect. It must be remembered that ragas and classical music should be played at the appropriate time to have maximum effect. Tests with the Lecher Antenna have established that a morning raga played in the evening or vica versa creates no improvement in the energy of the space or its alignment in the human body. Unlike Rock, however, it does not cause any ill effects either.

Terming its effects as intangible, powerful business interests who stand to lose millions of dollars if pill-popping is reduced, are not allowing society to experience the complete and profound benefits of music therapy. Unlike pills, good music has no side effects. It is effective because it heals the cause of the disease, rather than suppressing its effects, like modern medicine does. It restores the body's equilibrium, equanimity of the mind, emotional balance and mental prowess. Parameters like blood pressure pulse rate and EEGs show almost immediate and substantial improvement.

More and more hospitals, clinics and health centres are using music in ICUs and recuperation rooms, and reporting good results. More research needs to be carried out to determine specific sounds, tones and intonations to cure specific health conditions. Om, the Bija Mantra, Amen and other equivalents can be used for everything. This therapy, which was a major science of the past, is now poised to be the healing science of the future.

Conclusion

Music is life nourishing and the most appetizing food for the body, mind, heart and soul. It can keep our neighbours happy, our environment healthy, make plants grow and bring us peace.

11

The Miracle of Healing

The hand that
    Lifts the veil
        Of darkness
To let in revelation, light
    And joyous life
The touch, the word,
    And love—unfathomable
Rushes in
    Through the wedge of humility
        Beyond the walls of
            Ego and vanity
To give hope and dispel
    Pain, suffering and despair
The giver and the receiver
    Unify to create
        Another beginning.
A new dawn
    A new reality.

What do we need to do to be healthy in this era of stress, competition and pollution? Is good health a feasible notion at all or just a utopian dream?

The answer is simple. We merely need to want and decide to be healthy. Good health is not a boon that we need to struggle or strive for. It is our birthright.

In the preceding chapters we have discussed some of the ways in which elements, colours, gems, planets, spaces, rituals, symbols and sounds can be used to not only maintain our state of good health but to enhance our well-being. An attempt has been made to deal with logical and scientific ways of understanding them, identifying their causes and effects and identifying simple ways of harnessing and using them.

Do We Desire Good Health?

With so much at our beck and call we have a bouquet of health solutions to choose from, to remain healthy from here to eternity. In spite of that, however, this does not happen. Why? The problem is very basic. We do not want and choose to be healthy. The counter argument, of course, would be, 'what nonsense! Of course we all want to be healthy. We spend a lot of our time and money trying to do so'.

The natural tendency and inclination of a human body is to remain healthy. Those who find it difficult to believe this ought to observe children. They don't cry when they fall till a 'concerned' adult appears on the horizon and makes a fuss. Sometimes a child does not eat for the better part of the day because he or she is not hungry, whereas adults start feeling deprived and depressed if they do not sight food for more than six hours. Have you not noticed that children seem to have boundless energy? They never ever seem to get tired. By the time you realize they are tired, they are asleep. Lethargy is not part of the lexicon of a normal child. If a child can be healthy and energetic, it would make sense to presume that an adult with more sense, learning and a higher intake of food should be healthier. This, as we all know, does not happen. We harbour pre-conceived beliefs that as we grow older our health is bound to deteriorate.

Our lifestyle often belies our genuine interest in preserving good health. We form habits and behaviour patterns, which are born out of conditioning and peer pressure. We adopt a lifestyle which neither gives us good health nor pleasure. A mother, on the other hand, imbibes a belief in the child that milk and three meals a day is not only healthy but absolutely essential. She threatens him saying that if he does not drink milk, a ghost will appear! Fear is imbibed very early into the psyche of the child. Fear of darkness, of crossing the road, of being alone.

We actually start believing that it is very difficult not to have any illnesses and to be perfectly healthy. Even if we are apparently healthy and happy, we worry about the future. What will happen to our children if we do not earn enough money or if we die prematurely? Elation is momentary but fear stays with us like a true friend and companion. When we are in a state of ill health and sadness, we receive compassion and sympathy from others, whereas a healthy person is envied. Why on earth then would we ever want to be healthy and happy?

Why Are We Not Healthy?

We eat too much or too little; the food we eat is often short on nutrients and full of toxins. We no not sleep or exercise enough. Our work is stressful; the entertainment that we choose may not really be enjoyable. Why on earth do we behave in this manner? Because, over the years, we have disconnected with our body's antenna. We do not listen to what our body tells us. Our mind is too conditioned to think straight. We do things that we have been told to do and what seems to give everyone pleasure and not what we truly like. We have icons and idols who represent the worst values and examples that society has accepted.

When we stop hearing what our body tells us, disease (Dis-Ease) strikes. Illness is nothing else but time out—a time when we should reconnect with our body and understand what our mind was trying to tell us earlier. It's a time to reflect over the type of food, activity or thought that caused the disease, to enable us to not repeat the same behaviour pattern again. But that is not how we usually address illness. Instead, we pop a tablet, which is often prescribed to us by the chemist or the doctor on the phone, to ease the pain or infection so that we are able to get back to work or partying. What happens later? More often than not, the condition recurs. This time, we don't even need the doctor's help. We know the solution—the pill which worked earlier.

Disease and Treatment

Initially, the primary preoccupation is to correct the chemical imbalance that a disease has caused, and to kill the germs, cells and bacteria that are present with a mild or a strong drug. If a portion within the body is badly damaged, surgery ensures that the offending part does not affect the rest of the body. To put it simply, we treat the effect without understanding the cause. Invariably, like a bad penny, the disease reappears.

Moreover, modern treatment and surgery is inaccessible to a large number of people. It is more the preserve of the rich and famous. Medicines, doctors, hospitals and clinics are extremely expensive and often, commercially oriented.

The success of a doctor and hospital is linked to the number of patients admitted and discharged, and not how many of them are cured. If the patient is not healed, another array of medicines or tests is prescribed. Surgery is resorted to at the drop of a hat, instead of lifestyle correction. Life goes on. Breakthroughs in medical research are not benefitting the majority. Generally, their benefits are only available to the rich through a convoluted and collusive system of prescription, practice and patronage, which makes the doctors, surgeons and the medicine, medical equipment and implement makers richer.

On the brighter side, modern systems of medicine are now spending considerable amounts of money and time to understand the cause of diseases. Most medical research done recently is fascinating and path breaking. The number of people and institutions who are committing themselves with time and money to this marathon effort is increasing every day. Life-saving and longevity-enhancing solutions are definitely benefitting mankind. Relief from pain and increase in an active life span and productivity are some visible gains.

More and more people realize now that our ancient healing systems possessed accurate methods of diagnosis. They were not empirical in nature but recognized the functioning of the body systems as being distinct and unique for each person. Medicines made from plants and a diet and lifestyle correction regimen were prescribed. They were not, as was and is advocated by interested groups and corporate entities, 'unscientific'.

Ancient healing practices are again gaining more and more popularity and acceptance because they are simple, direct and effective. They show us ways of being healthy without spending heaps of money and going through innumerable tests and subjecting our body to strong chemical medication, which can have abominable side effects. They seek to understand the root cause of the problem and restore the body's ability to heal itself. Their medication is meant to rejuvenate the diseased cell and fight the bacteria, with a formulation of the same germ, as in the case of homeopathy,

Most medical practitioners admit that 95 per cent diseases are psychosomatic in nature, and medicines which either accelerate or retard the body's reactions and which give the body time and space to heal itself are prescribed.

Some techniques and methods, which apparently are less scientific and more esoteric than some of the concepts discussed in the preceding chapters, will be explored here. We find that more often than not, they can be used and administered without the help of experts and specialists.

In hospitals, most patients are referred to as a number and not by name. Standard cures are prescribed for certain symptoms without understanding the case history and the mental state or physiognomy of the patient.

On the other hand, in systems like ayurveda and homeopathy, a person's history of health, likes and dislikes, food and weather preferences, sleeping postures and habits, and innumerable other details are looked into. The body, mind and spirit are recognized as interconnected dynamic entities, which, for the same illness, respond to distinct healing methods and medication that can vary from person to person.

Recently, reports have appeared in the media about authentic scientific studies that show that homeopathic medicines have no real benefit and make people feel better only because of the placebo effect, a phenomena that makes us feel that we are feeling better because of conditioning or mindset. Well, if we can psyche ourselves to feel better mentally or homeopathically, nothing like it. Homeopathy was discovered, researched and developed in Germany, a country known for its scientific skills and achievements. I am sure that the Germans and many others, including us, are not going to allow such motivated and malicious propositions to be widely accepted.

Another recent development is even more disturbing. Canada has banned the import and sale of ayurvedic products and medicines alleging that they contain toxic materials like lead and arsenic which are harmful for human health. No facts to authenticate this finding have been given. Data on the deaths and illnesses caused is not available either. More lead and arsenic is found in drinking water than in these medicines. Cigarettes and alcohol are not banned. They are sold freely and advertised. This is a sorry example of the government of a state capitulating and abetting a group of people and companies who know that their enterprises will crumble and their millions disappear if ayurveda continues to make inroads into their markets.

Yoga, Pranayama, T'ai chi, Shiatsu, Acupressure

Systems like acupressure, acupuncture and reflexology attempt to align the subtle energy axis to empower the body to be healthy. The blood circulation is improved or restored to the dead or diseased cells of the body. These healing methods are based on the startling discovery that each part of the body has its corresponding points on various other parts of the body. Acupressure and acupuncture are based on the fact that each organ and part of the body is connected through a complex maze of nerves and meridians (naadis) to the soles and the sides of feet, the palms and fingers of hands, the outer ear and the spine. By stimulating or pressing these points with fingers or instruments, or by piercing special long needles on the hands, feet, ears and spine, almost all illnesses and discomforts can be treated.

Though it is quite safe and painless when done by a trained practitioner, many people are still apprehensive of being pierced with needles. Recently, electromechanical stimulators with probes that do not pierce the skin and can vary the pressure according to the sensitivity of the skin, have been developed. These can be used not only by trained acupuncturists, but by patients themselves after half an hour of practice and orientation.

Acupressure and acupuncture have been practised in China, India and parts of Africa for ages. With time, the practice has been further developed to make it more effective and user friendly.

Reflexology, as the name suggests, works on the principle of a stimulus or an action generating a response or a reaction. As per studies, many parts of the body have nerve ends or stimulus points on the legs and arms which are pressed to heal the affected part. In case of an injury, the affected part is not disturbed in order not to aggravate the injury and increase the pain and trauma.

While acupressure can safely be administered by the patients themselves with the help of charts or after initial guidance by an expert, at least on and for some parts of the body which can be accessed without discomfort, *acupuncture and reflexology should only be administered by an experienced practitioner*. In acupressure, when a point is pressed, pain will be felt if the corresponding part is diseased. We are required to press the point for ten to twenty seconds, release and press again. This can be repeated a few times. We will feel the pain easing at the pressed point and the discomfort and disease getting cured. However, no point should be pressed to an extent that causes unbearable pain and trauma.

Since acupuncture entails piercing the affected or corresponding part with long sharp needles, their incorrect use can cause injury. Of course, because of the direct and precise treatment, it can also give better and faster results as compared to the other two methods. It is amazing to behold how the whole procedure can be bloodless and painless.

Many people (including I) are doing acupressure on themselves every day for five-ten minutes for maintaining or enhancing their state of health and if required, for treating common colds, headaches, indigestion, insomnia and other common ailments and conditions which can cause considerable stress, agony and discomfort.

Major illnesses like cancer, spondylitis and tuberculosis can be cured by these practices. A question that I am often asked is whether we can combine yoga, reiki, shiatsu, acupressure and other treatments. The answer is a resounding Yes. They all complement each other wonderfully.

Yoga, pranayama, t'ai chi and shiatsu are ancient, time-tested practices which purify the vital energy of the body. The breathing techniques, postures and stretches maintain and enhance the health of the internal organs and the performance of the glands of the body. A yogi or a t'ai chi practitioner will have muscles which are stronger and more stress resistant than that of a weightlifter whose muscles are bigger. A yogi will be calmer and will have a lower pulse rate than an aerobics expert. Obviously, he is likely to live longer too.

Yoga, as is well known, is a practice which has made a permanent place for itself in the hearts and minds of all those who have explored and experienced its simple and wonderful effects. It is estimated that almost 5 per cent of the population in the US practises yoga. The number is increasing rapidly all over the world.

Yogasanas are postures and stretches that gradually increase the metabolic rate of the body and can exercise every part of the body, stretch and massage the internal organs and activate the glands of the body, without causing breathlessness and fatigue. The subtle body is also strengthened. While doing them, the person is taught to breathe correctly and normally. There are *asanas* designed for beginners, the obese and diseased, as also for the fit and agile. The sequence is designed to make a person relax between *asanas* to retain composure. It is most important to breathe correctly and normally during the exercises. It is not advised to hold one's breath. The sequence of various exercises should be such that the body parts are stretched in opposite directions. For example, exercises which arch the back need to be alternated with those that bend the back the other way. The most desired outcome is to make the body flexible and increase stamina.

Yoga activates and rejuvenates the cells of the body by injecting oxygen directly into them when they are stretched and more open. With age, the cells of the body lose their water retention capacity. This makes them dry and more susceptible to pain and discomfort. The resultant trauma makes the muscles stiffen and the arteries constrict, impairing movement and proper blood supply to the organs. Yoga overcomes this problem wonderfully.

It is normal to expect a yogi to live a disease-free life for more than 100 years. Yoga is not just an exercise regimen; it advocates a way of life which is simple and purposeful. It encourages people to eat less to remain more energetic, to drink a lot of water to cleanse the system of toxic wastes. In conjunction with pranayama, it enables a person to maintain a lower pulse and heart rate. During exercise and activity, the rate of increase of the pulse becomes lower and rate of recovery faster. The body is able to perform the same functions that it did earlier while maintaining a lower metabolic rate. This results in more energy availability to the body to digest food better and be active longer. Like yoga, pranayama also activates the cells and purifies the blood. The body and mind become completely relaxed.

A yogi aspires for and achieves a higher state of consciousness. He does not get angry and stressed even under extreme provocation and the most daunting circumstances. His calmness and state of equanimity has a salubrious effect on the surroundings and the people around. Those who question what is so special about yoga just have to look at any person who practises it regularly and they will get their answer. Their skin glows, the smile is wider, the demeanour is serene and nothing seems to rattle them. They seem to have more energy than most others.

Pranayama

Pranayama (regulated breathing) consists of a series of breathing exercises which rejuvenates every internal organ and nerve within the body. The toxins of the body and its aura are systematically expelled. The nostrils, mouth, heart and intestines are used in tandem. The breathing patterns are orchestrated to alternate between slow, rapid and holding cycles to create calm tranquility, make the head feel lighter, dissipate stress and create a feeling of expansion. Like yoga, pranayama rejuvenates the cells and purifies and detoxifies the blood. Contrary to popular belief, pranayama can also help in reducing the fat content in the body by increasing the metabolic rate and curing heart disease. This has been demonstrated by Swami Ramdevji, who in recent times, has taken yoga and meditation into millions of homes.

Pranayama can be practised as a complete regimen on its own or combined with yoga and other workout regimes. Diseases like colds, headaches, body pain and sinus can be cured quickly. The breathing cycles of 8-4-8-4, like the notes on a musical scale, create resonance and harmony within the body and increase its vibratory frequency, which makes it healthier and more energetic.

T'ai chi is a practice which was developed and has been practised in China for hundreds of years. It is now popular in many other parts of the world where it is being taught. As the name suggests, it harnesses and uses the power of 'chi' or subtle energy through postures, breath inhalation, exhalation and holding patterns to energize the body and balance the mind. Body posture, balance, flexibility and stamina are enhanced. T'ai chi is not as easy to learn as yoga. The practice of t'ai chi requires a lot of concentration and discipline. Obviously, the results that can be achieved are phenomenal. Its practitioners are known to transcend normal physical limitations with ease and are known to be capable of breathtakingly swift movements, exhibiting awesome strength and are highly intuitive. Regular practice also helps in increasing body immunity and resistance to illness by transmuting the quality of energy within the body and strengthening the aura or subtle body against bacteria, and, believe it or not, even against physical assault. People who have tried to attack a t'ai chi expert have recounted that they have felt as if they hit an invisible wall and hurt themselves.

T'ai chi is used extensively by martial arts experts both to defend themselves and as a form of counterattack.

It is quite normal to hear that a yoga or t'ai chi practitioner has never been ill.

Shiatsu, a Japanese word which means 'finger pressure', is a technique of healing which could be considered to be a combination of acupressure or acupuncture and massage. Pressure is applied to the body of the recipient with the palms of the hand, elbows, knees and feet depending on the extent of pressure required. Stretching and loosening up exercises are also prescribed to increase flexibility in ways similar to yoga. Shiatsu also works on the flow of chi, ki or prana that circulates through specific channels or meridians of the body.

The origins of shiatsu can be attributed to ancient Chinese medicine. The Yellow Emperor's *Classic of Internal Medicine*, written over 2000 years ago, reveals the causes of many illnesses and how to cure them, using changes in diet and lifestyle, and with acupressure and massage. The Chinese way of massage was practised mainly by blind people and known in Japan as *Anma*. New influences from Eastern traditions and Western sciences shaped *anma* into what is now known as shiatsu.

One of the reasons for the rapid rise in popularity of shiatsu is that it is effective in remedying many problems that Western medicine can do little for. Diseases like headaches, back pain, insomnia, chronic tension, painful periods, low vitality and depression have no real cures. What is often prescribed is a palliative to relieve or remove the pain. Shiatsu has given us the means to understand how certain imbalances in energy create these kinds of problems and provides ways to alleviate them. People who have taken treatment for a specific problem have experienced other benefits like better sleep, feeling more centred, calmer and brighter.

Can anyone learn shiatsu?

One does not require any special abilities to learn; of course those having experience in massage or in other forms of healing may learn faster. Shiatsu does not require great muscular strength and is not physically tiring for the giver.

It also works on the principles of the subtle body system and the chakras, connected through the meridians to the organs. Twelve main organs are described in Chinese medicine. Six of them, called ZANG, are concerned with the storage of energy; the other six are called FU and are concerned with transforming food into energy and excretion of waste products. Each of the twelve organs is linked with a meridian which traverses partly through the body and partly over the surface of the body. For example, the lung meridian travels through the lungs and the throat; it then emerges on to the surface in front of the shoulders and travels down the arm to the end of the thumb. On each meridian there are points which are useful in changing the energy flow in the whole meridian. They are called TSUBOS. They are not generally different from acupressure and acupuncture points. These meridians are normally bilateral, that is, they occur on both sides of the body.

Health is governed by the pattern of energy movement and the ease of its flow through the body. Energy flows also affect our moods, emotions and thinking.

Shiatsu treatment helps a person become deeply relaxed. When a person is relaxed he stops using up energy from within and receives more from outside.

How does one learn shiatsu?

The learning has to begin by people learning to feel energy (ki) between their hands and around another person. By redirecting ki with the mind people can even make themselves heavier or lighter. You may have noticed how a child who does not want to be picked up makes himself/herself feel very heavy. Even four people cannot lift a martial arts expert who knows how to control his ki. In Indian mythology, numerous examples abound of the use of shiatsu. An army of people in

Lanka, Ravana's kingdom, was unable to lift Lord Angad's foot off the ground.

Shiatsu is done with the receiver lying on the floor on a thin mattress, not immediately after or before taking a meal. Both the giver and the receiver should wear loose natural fibres in a warm room. The giver uses his body weight and not his muscular strength through the palms of his hand. The weight must be equally divided on both the hands and the giver should be comfortable. Fingers are not used for applying pressure. People can learn shiatsu by reading books and practising on others, and receiving regular feedback from them. It is important to talk to receivers and receive feedback.

Shiatsu can complement other types of healing and treatments very well and does not have ill effects since the feedback from the receiver is immediately available.

Sometimes shiatsu or other forms of healing like reiki and pranic healing may make people experience conditions or symptoms, which do not seem to be so welcome, such as tiredness, colds, headaches and release of emotions, or just feeling nothing at all. These are the result of the sudden release of energies or toxins stored deep down inside the body. The people who do not feel anything are normally those who have become quite insensitive. One cause of this insensitivity could be a diet high in animal fats and frequent intake of alcohol, which block the flow of ki.

As mentioned earlier, breathing is very important. In school during physical education, children are taught to keep the chest out and stomach in. They learn to hold their breath in their chest and exhale it from the chest. As a result it does not reach their abdomen. To know how to breathe correctly, watch a child breathing.

A complete shiatsu treatment comprises a sequence of about sixty-five stretches or presses. Some or all of it can be used at a time, depending on the time available and the problem.

Oriental Body Reading

In the oriental systems of healing, a patient's ailment can often be figured out and diagnosed by observing his posture, the way he holds his head, the position of his shoulder, etc. People who have headaches and migraines are often engaged in a lot of intellectual thinking. Those suffering from a stiff neck and shoulders are often those who eat lot of meat, eggs and dairy food, which affect the liver and the gall bladder. When a person's head droops forward, the lower back is found to be weak and the spine has an S shape. This could be due to the lungs and the large intestine being affected. The diseases associated with this are asthma, bronchitis, constipation and diarrhoea. This is normally caused by intake of excess sugar, sweets, chocolates, etc. Many other examples for almost each part of the body can be given.

The effects of all the above practices, which are both scientific and artistic, have been observed and recorded on camera. Their effects on people have also been tested extensively. There is now not even an iota of doubt that each oriental system of healing has many positive effects, which can enhance and transform our lives beyond recognition. Medical practitioners are learning to admire and accept the ways in which these practices can help their patients to recover faster and stay healthy.

Touch and Distant Healing

Other forms of healing, which are more unfathomable but are as or more effective, and which have existed for ages, have been rediscovered and are used extensively today.

Reiki, pronounced as Ray-Key, a hands-on healing technique, thousands of years old, is the Usui system for natural healing rediscovered by Dr Mikao Usui, a Japanese Buddhist, in the late nineteenth century. Following the formula he found in the Indian Sanskrit Sutras, he received the healing powers of reiki and the power of transferring this power to others.

Reiki can be defined as a Universal Life Force Energy. Reiki, the Usui system of natural healing, is not only the most simple and natural healing method we know of, but it is the most effective way of transferring this life force energy. Once a person has been opened up to become a 'channel' for reiki, concentrated life energy flows through his hands on its own accord and he retains this ability for the rest of his life.

Reiki is a powerful self-healing method that also promotes complete relaxation—'Rei' means Universal, and 'Ki' means Life Force. Ki is the non-physical energy used by all healers. Ki is all around us and can be accumulated and guided by the mind.

Reiki is the non-physical energy that animates all living things. As long as something is alive it has a life force circulating through it and surrounding it. When it dies the life force departs. If your life force is low or if there is a restriction in its flow, you will be more vulnerable to illness. When it is high and flowing freely, you are less likely to get sick. The life force plays an important role in everything we do. It animates the body and it is also the primary energy of our emotions, thoughts and spiritual life.

- Reiki supports the body's natural ability to heal itself.
- It heals on all levels whether mental, spiritual, physical or emotional.

- It loosens up blocked energy.
- It cleanses the body of all toxins.
- It increases intuitive awareness.
- It strengthens the immune system.
- Reiki helps one to meditate.
- It increases psychic sensitivity.

I have already recounted my tryst with reiki in the Introduction. For the last ten years, I have been giving myself reiki every day, not as a ritual, but because I need it the same way as I need to do my morning ablutions, if not more. I give reiki to others when it is sought, provided I am in a reasonably good state of physical, emotional and mental health.

Basic Concepts of Reiki

- Do not profess to be a doctor. We are merely channels and the patient heals himself or herself.
- Reiki is given only when asked for. It is not the duty of any healer to help where healing is not asked for or unwanted.
- There should be an exchange of energy for the healer's time. It could be in the form of gratitude or material objects, including money.
- A reiki channel's ability to heal depends on his attitude— it is effective only if given with unconditional love, humility and no expectations.
- Do not be attached to or anxious about the results. They depend upon the state of the patient, his or her readiness to accept it and other factors.

One can increase one's energy level and healing capacity by treating oneself daily and treating others whenever possible.

The Five Principles of Reiki

1. Just for today I will live the attitude of gratitude.

Let us always feel thankful for what we have as well as for what we know will constantly be provided. Our normal state is that of self-sufficiency or abundance. By living in gratitude, we eliminate want and a feeling of deprivation, and restore abundance.

2. Just for today I will not worry.

Worry results from a feeling of separateness from the universal wholeness. Let us try not to interfere with the universal timing of life, live each day to the best of our ability and the rest will be taken care of.

3. Just for today I will not anger.

Anger is a result of feeling out of control. When we get angry, we should become aware of our reactions and also feel thankful for having got an opportunity to look at our weakness. We need not feel guilty about experiencing anger. Instead, we should adopt the attitude of gratitude and just for today, not anger.

4. Just for today I will do my work honestly.

To be honest with ourselves is to face truth in all things. Truth brings clarity. Honesty with ourselves projects honesty on to others.

5. Just for today I will show love and respect for every living thing.

We are all from one source and are interdependent. To show love and respect to all others is to love and respect ourselves. What we give comes back to us manifold.

How Does Reiki Work?

Most people find it difficult to comprehend how it is possible to transfer healing energy by mere touch or by distant visualization. Actually we do not have to look or stretch our imagination too far to find many examples of how this can happen.

Have you seen a child who has been crying inconsolably for half an hour, instantly become quiet when the mother puts her hand on or caresses the child. Familiar healing energy is being transferred. It is not uncommon to see the same child gurgling and chortling within five minutes.

A microchip beams waves for thousands of miles that are processed by a receiver and translated into sounds, images and pictures. Why wouldn't a human mind that invented all this be able to transmit thought and healing energies to another being?

Giving and receiving energy is as simple as making a phone call. When the line is free, the call goes through. If not, it doesn't. Reiki uses power symbols strengthened over thousands of years by the applications of learned people and the faith of commoners. These symbols act as bridges, transmitters and receivers.

Learning Reiki

Learning Reiki is simpler than learning to write, read or walk. It is as simple as smiling. Reiki is taught by a reiki master who aquaints us with the hand positions on the body, the chakras and how they relate to the various organs of the body and their physiological and psychological functions and needs. To give the pupil a perspective of the origins of Reiki the 'reiki story' is also recounted. The most critical part is the attunement. Attunement is a process by which the reiki master reopens the channels of the pupil's energy body which have been blocked since childhood on account of emotions like fear, anger, greed and stress. Once opened and sealed in that position, the energy channels remain open forever.

A reiki channel, thereafter, simply has to invoke reiki energies. He or she can instantly feel the energy flow in the palm of the hands, the chest and the soles of the feet. A reiki attunement is therefore a gift, which once given by a reiki master to a reiki channel, can be put aside but cannot be thrown away or destroyed. Attunements affect each person differently, depending upon the vibratory level of their body cells.

The Reiki Story

To understand what the process of attunement is, why it is so powerful and how it was developed, we must be familiar with the 'reiki story'. Reiki owes its origin to the dogged and untiring perseverance of one man, Dr Mikao Usui.

Dr Usui was, by one account, a Christian missionary who taught school children in Kyoto. One day a student asked him if Jesus used to heal? If so, how? The noble teacher affirmed that indeed Jesus did heal and performed many miracles, but he had no idea how he did so. He promised only to come back to the class when he knew the answer. He asked all his seniors and other people in the Christian order of other countries for the answer. Nobody knew it. His quest led him to Buddhist monks, Tibetan monasteries and Indian sages. Often, when he looked at the Sutras, he felt he was close to finding the answer. After seven years he became demoralized and dejected. His guide and teacher suggested to him that he should do twenty-one days of meditation on top of Mount Fujiyama. He did so. After twenty days he was no wiser. He resolved that if he did not find the answer on the twenty-first day, he would end his life. At dawn at the end of the twenty-first day, he saw some bubbles on the horizon. Approaching nearer they looked similar to the Sutras he had seen and studied. Like boulders, they seemed to hit him and he was knocked unconscious. When he got up he remembered those visual shapes vividly but did not know what they meant and how to use them. However, like a child who has been gifted the most expensive toy on earth, his joy knew no bounds. He hurtled down the mountain and hit his toe against a boulder. In no time it was swollen like a pumpkin. Instinctively he put his hand on it and hey presto! the swelling disappeared. This was the first reiki miracle. On reaching a wayside restaurant at the foothills, being hungry he ordered a five-course meal and ate it. In sheer satisfaction, he rubbed his hands over his stomach, and was surprised to feel no indigestion. This was the second reiki miracle. When he was paying the bill he found the restaurant owner to be in great agony because of a swollen tooth. He visualized the symbols and put his hands on the swollen part of the restaurant owner's face, and lo and behold! the third miracle took place. As he went on perfecting his practice he developed a system of healing and attuning people, so they, in turn, could also heal.

While practising in a leper's colony he found that those he had healed returned after a year or two. They were happier begging rather that working! He realized that he had given them something without their asking for it. Reiki is not supposed to be given unless requested for or appreciated. He then went around villages to try and recruit committed and serious people to learn and carry forward this healing system. Every evening he would stand with a flaming torch in the village square and tell people his story, and perhaps conduct a healing. One of the people he recruited and who became his successor was Dr Chijuro Hayashi, who was a serving officer in the Japanese army. Clinics were opened in Tokyo and Osaka. A lady Doctor, Dr Hawayo Takata, who was terminally ill, came for treatment and was fully cured within one year. She decided to make this healing system her life's mission and became the first so-called reiki Grand Master. She returned to Hawaii, her hometown, and started perpetuating this practice there and in the US. One day she received a telepathic message from Dr Hayashi summoning her to Japan. When she reached there, she found him surrounded by his disciples and on the verge of giving up his own life. He explained to her that he had been called again by the army but could not now kill people and this would be construed as dereliction of duty. He was also apprehensive that reiki may not be encouraged in Japan and needed to be spread to other parts of the world, the responsibility of which he entrusted to Dr Takata. She, in turn, initiated another twenty-two Grand Masters who have spread reiki to many other parts of the world. Today we have hundreds and thousands of reiki channels who administer healing on themselves and on others in simple, inexpensive ways.

A reiki master attunes a person to be a reiki channel, if the latter wants to heal himself/herself and others. This is done by energetically reopening the blocked channels of the body and reactivating or switching on the memory receiver to receive and intuitively invoke reiki energies, and then pass them on to others by the touch of the hand or by using the mind as a transmitter. The reiki master is taught a method to do this. There are, of course, several methods. They all seem to work. What is important is the intent. Reiki helps and does the rest.

A strong indelible bond of deep love and compassion is established between a reiki master and his pupil as also between any giver and receiver.

Reiki and I

Why do I write in such detail about reiki, which can only be understood by receiving a reiki healing and not by words?

I do so because it changed me—my thoughts, actions, reactions and directions. It gave my creativity a sublime outlet and my life a definite purpose. It developed my intuitive and decision-making ability. I was able to learn more, share more with more, without shame and fear. It made me realize that there is no ideal state, no nirvana or ultimate salvation; that living is a process of looking at yourself again and again—of constant and perpetual cleansing. The more you scrub, the more muck will come out. The more sensitive you become, the more likely you are iikely to get hurt, feel pain. But getting hurt does not cause damage; it is a blessing that enables us to look at and address a problem. Living is all about understanding why we abuse our mind and our body and misbehave with and hurt others, especially those we love most. Living is about not feeling guilty and depressed about our mistakes and misbehaviour for the rest of our life. Reiki gives us the ability to begin the process of understanding the causes and healing the memories and conditions, which can include unresolved situations of past lives that make us form certain behaviour patterns and commit the same misdemeanours again and again.

Any one particular reiki channel cannot claim to possess higher skills and ability than another channel. Often, a first-level reiki practitioner can administer more effective healing than a reiki master. What makes the difference is the level of humility, extent of love and the connection with the healer.

Reiki was recommended to me seven days after I was diagnosed with tuberculosis on my back by a friend who wrote to me about the immense benefits that it had brought into her life. The reiki master informed us that after the two-day first-level workshop, we would have to give reiki healing to ourselves for twenty-one days without a break, for ninety minutes each day. Another person and I mentioned that we did not have that much time to spare. He advised us that if we did not have time for ourselves, we could leave after finishing our coffee. However, he also assured us that if we did venture to make a commitment to ourselves, reiki would create time for us.

I stayed and did the twenty-one days healing on myself. From the second day, my sleep reduced by ninety minutes to create time for me. After one month, my x-rays did not show any trace of the ailment. I was able to make better decisions faster, without apparently having to think. Reiki created time and the yearning to do and learn many other things at the same time, without creating any stress. Within six months, I had done the second and third-level reiki, all three levels of pranic healing, and a course in Arhatic Yoga with Master Choa Kok Sui, who developed the pranic healing system and propagated its benefits to more than fifty countries. I also did a course on geobiology and the use of the Lecher Antennae during this period—all this without neglecting my business.

Pranic Healing

Master Choa Kok Sui, a successful businessman based in the Philippines, sought and found answers beyond material comfort and possessions. He studied ancient Indian scriptures and practices and rediscovered the power to beckon energy from the cosmos. He used simple visualization techniques to cleanse the body and the aura and remove blockages, and to energize and heal.

A healer visualizes a white light or a cleansing colour like violet or green, projects it on the patient, and moves his hand anticlockwise around the part required to be cleaned to remove negative energies. These energies are thrown into a bowl of salt water. The healer, as in reiki, is taught how to sense and scan his own or another person's aura to determine which parts of the body are clogged with excess energy or depleted. After confirming his diagnosis with the patient, he decides the kind of healing required and that he will give. The hand is moved clockwise to energize a body part with the required colour or white light. Detailed procedures for healing various diseases, including cancer, are taught and are given in the books written by the Master. It is suggested that when a person is not certain about the colour to be used, white should be projected, since it contains all the colours. The body has the innate intelligence to choose the colour that it needs. Meditation techniques are also taught to help the healer to improve his own immunity and to protect him against the negative energies that he is subjected to during healing. Visualization exercises are also an integral part of the learning. Pranic healing is not an alternative to or a replacement for other forms of healing or medication. Like other non-obtrusive and nil side-effect techniques like yoga, reiki and shiatsu, it can complement homeopathy, ayurveda and even allopathic medicines.

The methods of healing described above are only those which I have experienced and benefitted from. There can be as many methods and techniques of healing as there are healers. What is important is the bond between the healer and the healed and the sincerity of intent. Even if the technique or the dose administered is not correct, nature and cosmic forces play a role to see that the patient is healed.

Food: The Gateway to Good Health

It is well known and accepted that more people die or suffer from illness because of excessive food intake rather than too little. Food is the most sought after commodity in the world—the pursuit or the consumption of which takes up the maximum amount of our time. We spend time in growing or buying food. We work so that we can provide food for us and our families. Wars are fought over food. We spend considerable time in cooking, serving and consuming food to indulge our taste buds, project our prosperity and please ourselves and our guests.

Our body needs food to provide us with energy to remain active and carry out our chores. Do you know which activity requires the maximum energy? Digesting food! The more we eat, the more energy we require to digest the food. Ten years ago, in spite of exercise and playing squash, I was at least 10 kg overweight. Extremely susceptible to colds, I suffered from one for around fifteen days every month. Providentially, I chanced upon *Fit for Life* by Marylene and Harvey Diamond. They explained in simple and interesting words and paragraphs, how the correct intake of food not only helps us in maintaining the optimum body weight, but also cures us of ailments and conditions we may have been living with for years.

Their stipulations were startling, to say the least. They struck at the roots of the beliefs and habits which had been passed on to me over the years by my parents and peers. As I read on, I discovered that what they were saying and the reasons they gave made so much sense that I followed about 60 per cent of their suggestions for the next three months and came up trumps.

I lost the excess baggage that I was carrying—all 10 kg, and got rid of a cold within hours instead of suffering for days and weeks.

The knowledge about food and nutrition was invaluable— do not have fruit after a meal; do not combine proteins with carbohydrates—no eggs with toast, fish with rice, milk with cereals, meat with potatoes. Only 23 gm of proteins are required by the body every day. Excess protein intake causes ill health. And so on . . .

Harvey explains that the human body is not designed for meat intake. Our teeth are for chewing, not shredding food. We have large intestines where food has to travel a long way. A carnivorous animal has canines, sharp teeth suitable for shredding meat which goes into a round stomach; its stomach contains acidic digestive juices which dissolve meat quickly. Our digestive juices are more alkaline than acidic. Harvey also counters the argument that meat makes the body stronger by pointing out that the strongest animals are vegetarians— elephants, buffaloes, oxen, horses. Archeological research into the fossil remains of our ancestors, thousands of years ago, proves conclusively that they were not only vegetarian, but only subsisted on fruits. And they were known to be much stronger than us!

The body is 80 per cent water. If we eat high water content food, it gets digested very easily. Fruits have 90 per cent water and vegetables almost 70-80 per cent. Even carnivorous animals eat the intestines, which comprise water, then the organs which have a high water content, and finally the meat, to the extent that they are still hungry. It must be remembered that having water with or after food or by itself does not provide the water for digestion. It is only meant for replacing water lost due to heat. In fact, water with or after food dilutes the digestive juices and causes indigestion. Water is best provided metabolically to the system through fruits and vegetables.

Urban dieticians often specify the correct amounts of proteins, minerals and carbohydrates that the body needs. What they often do not specify are the food combinations.

It is important to understand that nature has designed a way of absorbing and assimilating food which cannot be chemically simulated. It does not matter how much you eat, but what combinations you eat. Why is this vital? The intestines secrete digestive juices that are either acidic or alkaline, depending on the type of food that enters. If both types are eaten together, both types are secreted simultaneously and end up neutralizing one another. The secretion and neutralizing continues and it takes the body six-eight hours and considerable energy to digest the food. If, as it always happens, more food is eaten in the meantime, the rotting, fermented food is pushed out of the intestines and forms toxins and fat, leading to illness and obesity.

While fruit is the nectar of gods and human beings, it is lethal to have it after or with other foods. This is what 90 per cent of people do—they eat fruits anytime and especially after a meal. No wonder 90 per cent suffer from digestive problems. Fruits have acids which ferment other foods. They should only be had on an empty stomach—in the morning or at least four hours after a meal. Fruit on an empty stomach gets predigested and passes through the intestines in fifteen minutes, after which other foods can be eaten. It is a good idea to just be on a fruit diet for a week or for at least two-three days if the system has been overloaded for a few days. The toxic wastes in the body get cleaned up.

With the correct food combinations, since very little energy is used to digest the food, the balance available burns the fat and eliminates the toxicity in the body and makes us more energetic and active. If fish is to be eaten, it can taste equally good with vegetables. If proteins are eaten with starch or carbohydrates, make sure that you eat some vegetables with them. Vegetables lose their nutrition value when cooked: preferably try to eat them sautéed or steamed.

The virtues of milk and egg have been propagated and funded for the last hundred years by a cash-rich dairy and poultry industry in the west. In agrarian economies, where the cow is an object of worship, milk is used for making butter and ghee, a cooking saturate, in addition to being drunk. For people who are engaged in physical labour, milk is easily digested. For the city bred and all those who lead a sedentary lifestyle, milk causes serious digestive problems and mucous. This happens because milk contains casein, which is a thick gooey substance with adhesive properties. Casein lines the intestines and causes problems unless converted to perspiration by concentrated physical activity. A good test to determine whether a food is good for human consumption is to keep it in sunlight and see whether it starts smelling or putrefying. If it does, the same can be expected to happen inside you.

The body goes through three cycles: elimination, assimilation and absorption. Generally, the timings are 4 a.m. to 12 noon; 12 noon to 8 p.m., and 8 p.m. to 4 a.m. The elimination period is best for cleansing the body—taking a bath, doing morning ablutions and eating only fruits and drinking juices. The afternoon is a good time for eating. In all ancient civilizations, no food was eaten after sunset. The sun vitalizes the digestive system. During the night, when the body rests, food is assimilated and blood and tissue and cells are formed.

It is therefore a good idea to eat water-rich foods like vegetables with concentrated foods like breads and pizzas and nuts, or lentils or gram. In India rice and dal (lentil) is a staple food. It is advisable to mix some vegetables. Eating habits have also to be adapted to what is locally available and seasonal. Preserved and dried food has no nutritional value.

Conclusion

There are innumerable ways to remain healthy—good eating habits, exercise, self-healing, and correcting the effects of ill health by seeking help and self-correction. Our state of health and well-being is, more often than not, a fair indicator of our own self-esteem. If we like ourselves, we will want to look and feel good. And if we do not like ourselves and treat ourselves well, how and why ought we to complain about others not liking us or not behaving well with us.

Healing and charity are the best ways to correct our balance sheets and restore self-esteem. Try them as soon as you can.

References

Bodo J. Baginski and Shalila Sharamon, *Reiki: Universal Life Energy*, USA, Life Rhythm, 1988.

Barbara Ann Brennan, *Hands of Light: A Guide to Healing Through the Human Energy Field*, USA and Canada, Bantam Books, 1988.

Deepak Chopra, MD, *Quantum Healing: Exploring the Frontiers of Mind/Body Medicine*, USA and Canada, Bantam Books, 1989.

Oliver Cowmeadow, *The Art of Shiatsu*, UK, Element Books Limited, 1992.

Harvey and Marilyn Diamond, *Fit For Life II: Living Health, The Complete Health Program!*, UK, Bantam Books, 1988.

Gill Edwards, *Living Magically: A New Vision of Reality*, UK, Judy Piatkus Publishers Ltd, 1991.

Dr David Frawley, OMD, *Ayurvedic Healing: A Comprehensive Guide*, India, Motilal Banarsidas Publishers Pvt. Ltd, 1992.

Louise L. Hay, *You Can Heal Your Life*, UK, Hay House UK Ltd, 1984.

Choa Kok Sui, *The Ancient Science and Art of Pranic Healing*, Philippines, Health Accessories For All, 1990.

Neale Donald Walsch, *Conversations with God: An Uncommon Dialogue* (Book 3), USA, Hampton Roads, 1998.

Nancilee Wydra, *Feng Shui in the Garden: Simple Solutions for Creating a Comforting, Life-Affirming Garden of the Soul*, USA, Contemporary Books, 1997.